D1610820

What Price
Community Medicine?

By the same author

The Politics of Motherhood: Child and Maternal Welfare in England 1900–39 (Croom Helm, 1980)
Women's Welfare/Women's Rights (ed.) (Croom Helm, 1983)
Women in England. Sexual Divisions and Social Change, 1870–1950 (Wheatsheaf Books, 1984)
Labour and Love. Women's Experience of Home and Family 1850–1940 (ed.) (Blackwell's, 1986)

What Price Community Medicine?

The Philosophy, Practice and
Politics of Public Health since 1919

Jane Lewis

Lecturer in Social Science and Administration
London School of Economics

WHEATSHEAF BOOKS

First published in Great Britain by
WHEATSHEAF BOOKS LTD
A MEMBER OF THE HARVESTER PRESS PUBLISHING GROUP
Publisher: John Spiers
16 Ship Street, Brighton, Sussex

British Library Cataloguing in Publication Data

Lewis, Jane
    What price community medicine? : the
    philosophy, practice and politics of
    public health since 1919
    1. Community health services—Great
    Britain—History—20th century
    2. Medical care—Great Britain—
    History—20th century
    I. Title
    362.1'0425   RA485
    ISBN 0-7450-0349-4

Typeset in 11/12pt Times British
Printed and bound in Great Britain by
Billing & Sons Limited, Worcester.

THE HARVESTER PRESS PUBLISHING GROUP
The Harvester Group comprises Harvester Press Ltd (chiefly
publishing literature, fiction, philosophy, psychology, and science
and trade books); Harvester Press Microform Publications Ltd
(publishing in microform previously unpublished archives, scarce
printed sources, and indexes to these collections); Wheatsheaf
Books Ltd (chiefly publishing in economics, international politics,
sociology, women's studies and related social sciences).

Contents

Acknowledgements   vii

Introduction: Public health, medicine and the state   1

1. The divorce between the theory and practice of
    public health 1919–1950   15

2. Pressure from within and without: public health
    1950–1968   57

3. From public health to community medicine: the
    making of a new specialty 1968–1974   100

4. A decade of community medicine 1974–1984   125

5. What price community medicine?   160

Appendix I: The public health responsibilities of local
    government 1929–1974   165

Index   167

Acknowledgements

My sincere thanks go to the Society of Community Medicine and in particular to Dr Peter Gardner for helping me to locate so many medical officers who became community physicians in 1974; to all those practising and retired community physicians who generously shared their experiences with me; to the many archivists and librarians who have helped me, especially those at the Wellcome Institute for the History of Medicine, the BMA, and the London School of Hygiene and Tropical Medicine; to the Wellcome Unit for the History of Medicine at Oxford for their support and advice; to the Social Sciences and Humanities Council of Canada for financial support; and finally to Professor Brian Abel-Smith and Dr Charles Webster for generously reading the manuscript for me.

Introduction: Public health, medicine and the state

The term public health invariably conjures up images of the heroic nineteenth-century battles to provide sewerage and clean water, led by figures such as Edwin Chadwick, William Farr and Sir John Simon. Unlike twentieth-century civil servants, these men were zealots,[1] seemingly unafraid of taking a strong stand and pursuing their own policies. However, after the grosser environmental problems of the rapidly expanding towns came under control, the popular image of public health and its practitioners fades. It is perhaps fortunate that the obstructionist and dreary character of Dr Snoddy in the popular television series of the late 1960s and early 1970s, 'Dr Finlay's Casebook', was not widely recognized as a public health doctor. His portrayal could not have been more remote from that of a battling pioneer.

Public health has also slipped out of the best recent analyses of the contemporary history of health professions and health services. F. Honigsbaum's account of the 'division in British medicine' concentrates on the split between GPs and consultants, and R. Klein's account of the politics of the NHS pays little attention to public health.[2] Yet public health departments existed as part of local government until the 1974 reorganization of the NHS, presided over by medical officers of health. They were responsible for implementing the Public Health Acts, covering matters such as water, food and sanitation; for the notification of infectious diseases; for clinics screening mothers and children, TB and VD patients; and, from 1929 until 1948, for the administration of municipal hospitals. Traditionally, these services, with the exception of hospitals, have been labelled 'preventive medicine', and to run them MOsH and large staffs of nurses, health visitors, public

1

health inspectors and, increasingly in the 1960s, social workers.

In 1974, the MOH and the public health department disappeared, the vast majority of MOsH becoming community physicians, who were appointed at each of the three levels of the new NHS structure. Community physicians retained responsibility for advising local authorities in respect of the various services (for example, maternal and child welfare) that had been administered by MOsH, but the supervision of environmental health, the most longstanding responsibility of public health, passed to the environmental health officers, who continued to work with the local authorities. The tasks of the community physician were defined largely in relation to the need of the new NHS for someone who would stimulate effective integration of the hitherto separate services—general practitioner, hospital and local authority—and undertake to provide the information necessary for planning.

According to T. McKeown, improvements in health status over the last two centuries have owed more to better living standards than anything else, and more to public health measures than to curative medicine.[3] Yet the NHS has, from its inception, been dominated by the hospital. In the early 1970s, there was a revival of interest in preventive medicine, accompanied by a government commitment to redistribute resources away from the acute sector to the priority 'Cinderella' services for the mentally ill, the chronically sick and the handicapped and disabled. The renewed interest in 'prevention and promotion' focused on securing healthy lifestyles for individuals rather than on environmental issues or structural variables, and was prompted more by a desire to prevent people becoming hospital patients—in other words, to cut hospital costs—than to reorient the whole nature of medical practice.

The question remains, what happened to public health after its first full flowering in the nineteenth century? Are we to conclude that it failed to provide any real alternative either by way of an approach to health problems or as a model for the delivery of health services? The answer is yes on both counts, although in respect to the latter, it is arguable that the public health system had provided a basis for a national system of health services by the 1930s but that this was passed over when the NHS Act was formulated for medico-political reasons. However, this is a sub-plot, for the most important failure of public health was its lack of a firm philosophy to guide it in approaching health problems. During the early twentieth century, those active in the field worked out what looked very much like an *ex post facto* rationalization of public health's increased involvement in the work of personal, preventive services, further legitimated by the histories of public health written by practitioners.[4] After World War II, public health allowed itself to become defined by the activities it undertook. The idea of public health thus remained indistinct. In part this was due to a failure on the part of public health practitioners to recognize the need for a coherent philosophy. However, it is also the case that if public health attempts to adopt a broad mandate—to secure, for example, 'healthy public policy'—it inevitably encounters conflict with the medical profession, government and industry. The broad vision of the nineteenth-century public health pioneers was the product of a particular set of historical circumstances, which permitted health reform to act as an umbrella for other social questions. It was not an intentionally radical vision. Public health in the nineteenth century was, and has remained, firmly under government direction and control and, as community medicine, continues to occupy a subservient position within the medical profession.

The central question addressed in this book is therefore what public health and community medicine have been concerned about and why. The focus of the analysis is thus on the constraints experienced by public health in the form of, first, its own failure adequately to conceptualize its activities; second, the way in which the concerns of public health have been structured by the concerns of government; and third, the medical politics of public health doctors' position in relation to the rest of the medical profession, and of public health practice in relation to hospital-dominated medical care. In brief, it will be argued that before 1974 the idea of public health had substantially narrowed, despite the fact that it enjoyed extensive statutory powers which enabled public health departments to deliver a wide range of health care services, particularly during the period 1929–48. The idea of community medicine represented an attempt to give conscious direction to public health practice and to broaden its concerns, but it has in large measure been frustrated by the nature of community medicine's position within the NHS.

PUBLIC HEALTH AND THE STATE

In large part the practice of public health was always governed by legislation, first by the Public Health Acts, and after 1946 by the NHS Act. In fact, public health as a form of state regulation has a remarkably long history. C. Cipolla has described the efforts of the seventeenth-century Italian city states to control the spread of plague, and G. Rosen, the operations of the 'medical police' in continental Europe during the eighteenth century.[5] These attempts to exert control over urban populations were often ruthless; quarantines were imposed and cleansing ordered (including the burning of personal possessions) without the victims being compensated.

During the nineteenth century, industrialization and rapid urbanization made more extensive and more formal protection of the community necessary. State intervention went furthest in matters of health policy, largely because of the threat diseases such as cholera and smallpox posed to the whole community. Indeed, vaccination against smallpox was the only measure that central government made the obligatory responsibility of local authorities.[6] However, nineteenth-century governments still preferred an *ad hoc* response to health problems. The Central Board of Health, set up in 1848, was abandoned in 1854, and its responsibilities transferred to the Privy Council and later again to the Local Government Board. Despite the recommendation of the Sanitary Commission of 1869 in favour of a Ministry of Health, none was set up until 1919. Primary responsibility for health initiatives rested at the local level, where the Public Health Act 1872 made the appointment of an MOH obligatory for local sanitary authorities in England and Wales, and the Local Government Act 1888 permitted the new county councils to do likewise (they were not compelled to do so until 1909). MOsH were charged with enforcing the public health acts in their communities, for inspecting food, sanitation and housing, and for publishing an annual report on their activities and the state of the public health in their communities.

'Slum' and 'fever den' were terms used interchangeably in the nineteenth century.[7] Both they and their inhabitants were feared as agents of infection before it was understood how this occurred. As P. Starr has pointed out, all dirt was considered dangerous.[8] By the end of the century, social investigators were convinced that physical well-being was a necessary prerequisite for further social progress. The urban environment was feared to be producing a rate of degenerates, physically stunted and morally inferior.[9] The slippage between social and moral categories, so characteristic of Victorian social science,[10] only served to intensify the fear of contamination. Fear, together with religious zeal and civic pride (albeit often moderated by ratepayer parsimony) combined to effect the sanitary reform associated with the early public health movement. The major public health acts of the nineteenth century were also characteristically housing acts.

While the focus of nineteenth-century public health seems clear, writers have found it hard to describe the content of public health in the twentieth century. C.-E.A. Winslow, the early twentieth-century American authority on public health, identified three phases in the development of public health: the first, from 1840 to 1890, was characterized by environmental sanitation; the second, from 1890 to 1910, by developments in bacteriology, resulting in an emphasis on isolation and disinfection; and the third, beginning around 1910, by an emphasis on education and personal hygiene, often referred to as personal prevention.[11] This chronology is broadly congruent with developments in Britain.[12] Beyond the period examined by Winslow, the 1930s added a large administrative responsibility in the form of the municipal hospitals, which was not wholly compatible with the focus on personal prevention, while the post-war period subtracted the responsibility for both hospitals and clinics, leaving the MOH in more of a co-ordinating and administrative role in respect to community health services.

Despite a dramatic growth in the statutory powers of public health departments, twentieth-century developments resulted in a narrowing of public health's mandate. Scientific advances in bacteriology redefined the kind of intervention appropriate for public health. Once it was realized that dirt *per se* did not cause infectious disease, the broad mandate of public health to deal with all aspects of environmental sanitation and housing as the means of promoting cleanliness disappeared. Germ theory deflected attention from the primary cause of disease in the environment and from the individual's relationship to that environment, and made a direct appeal from mortality figures to social reform much more difficult.[13] Increasingly public health authorities focused on what the individual should do to ensure personal hygiene. No clearer example of the effects of this approach can be found than the campaign to reduce infant mortality. Epidemiological studies of the problem conducted in the late 1900s revealed the death rate to be highest in poor inner city slums, yet public health physicians focused their attention almost entirely on health education, encouraging mothers to breastfeed and strive for higher standards of domestic hygiene.[14] Public health justified its increased emphasis on clinic work with mothers and children as 'applied physiology', a new kind of preventive clinical medicine. But this philosophy could not survive the transition to the NHS and the subsequent claim of GPs to do the work.

P. Starr has characterized the shift in the changing nature of public health work in the twentieth century as a move towards a 'new concept of dirt'.[15] As a result of germ theory, the twentieth-century concept of dirt 'narrowed' and also proved considerably cheaper to clean up. This analysis is valuable for the way in which it acknowledges the importance of the political imperative to a more limited, less costly, mandate for public health, in addition to that of developments in medical science.

It is crucial to relate the changing direction of public health to the changing nature of state intervention in social issues. The nineteenth-century vision of public health was broad because the Public Health Acts were permitted to serve as a filter for more general social reform.[16] As A. Sutcliffe has perceptively argued, the 'urban variable' acted as a spur to state intervention because a large number of social questions concerned with poverty and housing as well as health were packed into the fear of urban degeneration and physical deterioration.[17] The vision of nineteenth-century public health was broad not least because in the period before these other social policy issues entered the realm of 'high politics',[18] public health legislation provided the only legitimate means of attacking them. The existence of such a broad vision does not necessarily mean that proponents of health were bent on pursuing an optimal strategy to secure the health and welfare of the people. It would be more accurate to describe nineteenth-century aims as minimalist, designed to secure a functioning working population. Chadwick, after all, was inspired to action on health reform by the idea that disease brought large numbers on to the poor law. Nineteenth-century public health measures isolated infectious people and began clearing the slums that were the product of poverty, but made no attempt to tackle the issue of poverty directly. Public health was defined in such a way that a wide range of social issues fell within its compass, but this did not mean that its proponents saw it necessary to take positive action to tackle them or to put accountability to the people before accountability to the state.

During the Edwardian period, the years of the Liberal welfare reforms, not only was there more legislative activity in the field of social policy—the centrepiece being the introduction of national insurance for periods of sickness and unemployment in 1911—but health and welfare were firmly separated and a tighter mandate imposed on both. Thus in narrowing its focus, public health was arguably responding to the changing framework of state intervention as well as to changes in medical science. The calls that have been made periodically during the first decade of community medicine's existence for it to rethink its mandate in respect to responsibility for environmental hazard and the structural variables crucial to the prevention of disease and the promotion of health, actually represent a new departure, even though reference is often made to the nineteenth-century public health movement. Such a focus would necessarily involve political confrontation.[19] The nineteenth-century sanitarians were not afraid to tackle water companies and other vested interests, but it was not part of their plan to change radically the social and political fabric.

THE MEDICAL POLITICS OF PREVENTION VERSUS CURE

The status of public health doctors in the twentieth century has been low, and a major part of the story of public health has been the struggle of doctors in the field to achieve a professional status comparable to other members of the medical profession. As the vision of public health narrowed to focus more firmly on individual personal prevention, so it became more necessary to delineate the legitimate work of the public health doctor from that of other practitioners, particularly the GP. The result was what has commonly been described as the separation of 'prevention from cure'.[20] (Of course, the ability of doctors to effect cures increased dramatically in the early twentieth century.) In terms of medical politics, there is no doubt as to the reality of the separation. This was due in part to the perceived threat that the local authority clinic posed to the independent practitioner and in part to the difficulties experienced by public health in achieving specialist status (a problem shared by GPs). Both these factors must be related to the failure to evolve a firm philosophy for public health work. The *ex post facto* rationalization of clinic work as a special kind of preventive clinical medicine was not accepted by other members of the medical profession who found it too easy to condemn public health as a species of straightforward medical practice controlled by the state.

In the heroic decades of the mid-nineteenth century public health had also been preoccupied with eliminating disease, rather than promoting health, but, because of its primary focus on environmental sanitation and its status as a broadly-based social reform movement it had not come into direct conflict with fellow members of the medical profession. There is little evidence of British public health doctors developing an analysis comparable to that of Virchow in mid-nineteenth-century Germany, who recognized that the promotion of health involved social as well as medical factors.[21] Indeed the development of germ theory encouraged public health doctors in the search for the medical cause of disease. The concept of social medicine did not develop in Britain until the late 1930s and 1940s, and then was confined in large part to university departments. Throughout the 1950s and 1960s there continued to be little real contact between university departments and practitioners.

The preventive medicine of the early twentieth century focused on the early diagnosis of disease, and it is difficult to draw a firm dividing line between it and curative medicine. Writing on the work of MOsH in London between 1856 and 1910, A. Wilkinson has expressed the opinion that:

The extension of preventive medical concern to the detail of family domestic habits in the course of the 1890s marks the final maturing of preventive consciousness in the ninteenth century. From the early concentration on the externals of a healthy life, through the realisation of channels of infection, to the conclusion that the habits of ordinary people were crucial to their welfare, the MOsH in their first fifty years of existence made a substantial contribution to the evolution of the preventive idea.[22]

However, while it may be accepted that the focus of public health work shifted to personal hygiene and health education, there was little sign of the preventive idea developing beyond the aim of securing national efficiency. Furthermore, the preoccupation of public health departments with the problems of mental deficiency and TB during the 1930s indicates that this continued to be the case. The professional organizations of public health doctors gave no indication of subscribing to a positive idea of health or of wishing to change the nature of medical practice, although a few individuals showed themselves to be susceptible to the pressure for reform which emanated from outside the medical profession with people such as the founders of the Peckham Health Centre, an independent research experiment designed to test ideas regarding the nature of health and the conditions necessary for its maintenance.

Considerable enthusiasm for public health as preventive medicine was expressed during the early twentieth century, particularly by Sidney and Beatrice Webb, but their chief concern was the organization of medical services and access to medical care, not the practice of medicine. They saw the local public health departments as a key to breaking up the poor law and listed three ways in which public health work was superior to poor law medicine: first because of its educational value, second because it drew on the voluntary sector, and third because it served to stimulate self-respect, parental responsibility and maternal care.[23] In other words, the Webbs were deeply sympathetic to the concern about national efficiency that underpinned so much of early twentieth-century public health work. In fact, their enthusiasm for the public health sector only served to underline the lack of any real philosophical basis for the division between preventive and curative medicine.

By the 1930s relations between MOsH and GPs in particular were singularly strained, with GPs accusing public health clinics of 'encroaching' on private practice. In the 1840s the professional position of doctors had been 'marginal'; Chadwick's own preference for engineers over doctors is well known. As a result, medical practitioners had been glad to accept low status, part-time salaried positions as poor law medical officers in the service of the state.[24] By the early twentieth century this was no longer the case; indeed some MOsH opposed the granting of a statutory right to security of tenure under the Health and Town Planning Act 1909 because they wanted to retain a foothold in private practice.[25]

The medical profession has always regarded methods of payment as crucial to the maintenance of professional autonomy. Independent practitioners regarded MOsH as a threat because of their position as salaried employees. In the 1930s, MOsH believed that the public health model of health service delivery, which had by that time extended to include the municipal hospitals, would provide the basis for any national health service. In fact, the government decided against local authority control of the new service; guaranteed the status of the GPs as independent contractors; modelled the new hospital management committees on the scheme of management used in the voluntary hospitals; and reduced the responsibilities of the public health department. It may therefore be argued that the NHS Act 1948 represented a victory for the mainstream of the medical profession.

THE POST-WAR VACUUM

When public health was forced to retrench after 1946 and to confine its activities to what was initially a rather narrower set of extra-hospital services, the vacuum in public health philosophy became even more evident. As L. Jordanova has remarked, public health came to resemble a 'ragbag' of activities.[26] Moreover, it was forced to search for a new identity within the framework of a rigid and unreformed local government structure. The civic pride of the nineteenth century had given way to municipal decline.

The move to reform public health was led by academics in the field, who sought to provide a new rigorous training in health administration, and by the new epidemiology, which sought to apply the epidemiology method to all forms of disease behaviour, although D. Roth has argued that it too has been severely restricted by its lack of theoretical context.[27] Proponents of community medicine used the argument that the barrier between prevention and cure was crumbling to promote the integration of public health into the NHS, with the community physician providing the information for the efficient and effective administration of the service and co-operating closely with clinicians. When community physicians were appointed in 1974, the transition from public health to community medicine was welcomed by the vast majority of public health doctors, mainly because they were in favour of integrating general practitioner, hospital and local authority services, but also because they stood to gain specialist status as community physicians.

Yet the specialty of community medicine was born more of administrative fiat than of medical advance or professional strength. Its identity and its future were intimately bound up with the new structure of the NHS. Furthermore, government policy-makers were more concerned with the contribution the specialty could make to the effective integration of the health services and in particular to the elaborate machinery for achieving consensus management, than they were with the goals that should be set for the developing of the new specialty. The reorganization of the NHS was a product of faith in an 'organizational fix'[28] that extended beyond the health service to the reform of the personal social services and of local government, and beyond Britain to other western countries during the late 1960s and early 1970s. Community medicine was deeply embedded within its managerial philosophy. Not surprisingly, the chief subject of debate within the new specialty has been the direction it should take. In addition, the status of community physicians in the eyes of their colleagues has remained low, despite their specialist status. It was, after all, unrealistic to expect senior public health doctors either to begin to behave differently or to be perceived differently by their colleagues after one or two short training courses and a change in title.

The major sources of tension that continue to be experienced by community physicians reflect the longstanding problems of public health in terms of its relationship to the state and to the rest of the medical profession. Government policy-makers were hopeful that the community physician would be primarily a manager, working within the NHS bureaucracy, looking at the need for medical services in a particular community and recommending a more rational allocation of resources at one with the government's stated desire to give more support to 'Cinderella' services. But this took community medicine further than ever from the idea that the concern of public health was the health and welfare of the people, and threatened to turn the community physician into someone concerned above all with the efficient management of services. Much of the debate in the community medicine literature has been about how the community physician may best advise on health problems and health needs, and how he/she might become more accountable to the local community. But community medicine faces the problem that the adoption of a broader mandate would inevitably entail political conflict. Furthermore, to be successful, community medicine would have to be treated 'not so much as a specialty within medicine as the way in which health services should be considered within a welfare state',[29] but this is immediately to invoke the other major spectre of medico-political conflict.

NOTES

1. H. Parris, *Constitutional Bureaucracy* (London: Allen & Unwin, 1969).
2. F. Honigsbaum, *The Division in British Medicine* (London: Kogan Page, 1979); and R. Klein, *The Politics of the NHS* (London: Longmans, 1983).
3. T. McKeown, *The Modern Rise of Population* (London: Edward Arnold, 1976).
4. E.g. G. Newman, *The Rise of Preventive Medicine* (Oxford: Oxford University Press, 1933); and A. Newsholme, *Medicine and the State* (London: Allen & Unwin, 1932).
5. C. Cipolla, *Cristofano and the Plague* (Berkeley, Cal.: UCLA Press, 1973); G. Rosen, *From Medical Police to Social Medicine* (New York: Science History Publications, 1974).
6. R. Lambert, 'A Victorian NHS', *Historical Journal*, 5 (1962).
7. A. Wohl, *Endangered Lives: Public Health in Victorian Britain* (Cambridge, Mass.: Harvard University Press, 1983), p. 45.
8. P. Starr, *The Social Transformation of American Medicine* (New York: Basic Books, 1982).
9. Wohl, *Endangered Lives*, p. 6. *See also* G. Stedman Jones, *Outcast London* (Harmondsworth: Penguin, 1971), and C.F.G. Masterman, *The Heart of Empire* (Brighton: Harvester, 1973).
10. E.P. Hennock, 'Poverty and social theory in England: the experience of the 1880s', *Social History*, 1 (1976).
11. Starr, *Transformation of American Medicine*, p. 191.
12. D.E. Watkins, 'The English Revolution in social medicine, 1880–1911', unpub. Ph.D. thesis, University of London, 1984, p. 10.
13. N. Hart, *The Sociology of Health and Medicine* (Ormskirk, Lancs.: Causeway Books, 1985), pp. 14–17. *See also* J.P. Eyler, *Victorian Social Medicine* (Baltimore: John Hopkins University Press, 1979) and F.B. Smith, *The People's Health* (London: Croom Helm, 1979).
14. J. Lewis, *The Politics of Motherhood* (London: Croom Helm, 1980).
15. Starr, *Transformation of American Medicine*, p. 189.
16. E.J. Higgs, 'The construction of statistics: the struggle for occupational census, 1841–1911', in *Government Expertise*, ed R.M. MacLeod (Cambridge: Cambridge University Press, forthcoming).
17. A. Sutcliffe, 'In search of the urban variable', in *The Pursuit of Urban History*, eds D. Fraser and A. Sutcliffe (London: Arnold, 1983).
18. The phrase is J. Harris's, 'The transition to high politics in English social policy', in *High and Low Politics in Modern Britain*, eds M. Bentley and J. Stevenson (Oxford: Clarendon Press, 1983).
19. See the argument in M. Renaud, 'On the structural constraints to state intervention in health', in *The Cultural Crisis of Modern Medicine*, ed J. Ehrenreich (New York: Monthly Review Press, 1978).
20. Starr, *Transformation of American Medicine*, p. 196; Watkins, 'The English revolution in social medicine', p. 15–16.
21. Rosen, *From Medical Police to Social Medicine*, pp. 60–119.
22. A. Wilkinson, 'The beginning of disease control in London: the work of

the medical officers in three parishes, 1856–1900', unpub. D. Phil. thesis, University of Oxford, 1980, p. 320.

23. S. and B. Webb, *The State and the Doctor* (London: Longmans, 1910), pp. 179–80.

24. I. Inkster, 'Marginal men: aspects of the social role of the medical community in Sheffield, 1790–1850', in *Health Care and Popular Medicine in Nineteenth Century England* (London: Croom Helm, 1977); J. Peterson, *The Medical Profession in Mid-Victorian London* (Berkeley, Cal.: University of California Press, 1978) and S.J. Novak, 'Profession and bureaucracy: English doctors and the Victorian public health administration', *Journal of Social History,* 6 (1973); A. Crowther, *The Workhouse System, 1834–1939* (London: Batsford, 1981), p. 158.

25. Watkins, *The English Revolution in Social Medicine*, p. 199.

26. L. Jordanova, 'Review essay', *Social History* 6 (1981).

27. D. Roth, 'The scientific basis of epidemiology: an historical and philosophical enquiry', unpub. Ph.D. thesis, University of California at Berkeley, 1976, pp. 51 and 131.

28. The term is Klein's, *Politics of the NHS*, p. 90.

29. H. Francis, 'Towards community medicine: the British experience', in *Recent Advances in Community Medicine*, ed A.E. Bennett (Edinburgh: Livingstone, 1978), p. 14.

1 The divorce between the theory and practice of public health 1919–1950

During the 1920s and 1930s the work of the local public health departments grew significantly in range and importance. Between 1918 and 1939 some twenty pieces of legislation benefiting local health authority services were passed, and C. Webster has estimated that the setting-up of the NHS in 1948 resulted in only a fractional increase in the amount of GNP spent on the provision of state medical services.[1] Furthermore, most of the interesting initiatives in health service provision—in school health and the building of early health centres, for example—were undertaken by public health departments. By 1939 local authorities were permitted to provide maternal and child welfare services, including obstetrical and gynaecological specialist treatment (under the Midwives Act 1936); a school medical service, including clinics treating minor ailments; dentistry; school meals and milk; TB schemes, involving sanatorium treatment, clinics and aftercare services; infectious disease, ear, nose and throat and VD services; and health centres, the most elaborate being that built by the Finsbury Borough Council in 1938. In addition the Local Government Act 1929 allowed local authorities to take over the poor law hospitals and, by 1938, the number of acute beds provided by local authorities equalled that provided by the voluntary sector. Finally, the Cancer Act 1939 placed responsibility for the development of local regional cancer schemes on the local authorities rather than on the voluntary hospitals.*

It is, perhaps, not surprising that one commentator. has regarded the inter-war years as the 'golden age' of public

---

*Appendix 1 summarizes the public health responsibilities of local government for the period 1929–74.

health.[2] Certainly public health doctors exhibited great confidence during the period, expressing the belief that the medical services would become increasingly state-controlled and that this would inevitably mean a more powerful public health sector. In fact, the NHS Act 1946 substantially dismantled the public health departments, leaving them with responsibility for domiciliary midwifery, health visiting and nursing services, vaccination and immunization, ambulance services, and environmental hygiene. Most public health doctors bewailed 'the remnants that remain'[3] and noted correctly that with the loss of municipal hospitals and TB, cancer and clinic services, the only hope the public health service had of rebuilding its empire rested with the promise to build health centres.[4] But as it transpired, this promise remained unfulfilled until the late 1960s, by which time public health departments were struggling to meet the demands of the NHS for 'community care' provision and were facing a new threat of decimation from the Seebohm Committee's recommendation that social work services be removed from their control.[5]

Measured solely in terms of power and influence, there can be no doubt but that the public health departments suffered substantial diminution in 1948, but this raises questions regarding the fundamental nature and direction of public health work during the inter-war years. It will be argued here that public health practice had no clear philosophy during this period. There was considerable discussion as to the meaning of 'preventive medicine' in the public health journals during the inter-war years, and some misgivings about the increasing involvement of public health doctors in hospital administration after the passing of the Local Government Act of 1929, but on the whole the aims of public health seem to have been formulated *ex post facto*, justifying the expanding interests of MOsH, first from environmental to personal health care services (chiefly for mothers and children and for TB and VD patients) and later to hospital administration. The public health departments added to their domain without questioning what was distinctive about public health. New thinking about health as opposed to sickness, and about the determinants of both, came not so much from the public health practitioners as from privately-funded experiments, like the Peckham Health Centre; pressure groups, such as the Women's Health Inquiry and the Children's Minimum Council; and, most importantly, from the point of view of the public health practitioner, from academics in medical and social science, who began talking in the 1940s about the importance of a concept they called social medicine rather than public health. It is significant that MOsH were at first puzzled by the discussion of social medicine and by the late 1940s had rejected it.

Two major practical problems followed from public health's failure to establish a firm philosophical base for its activities. First, its preoccupation with the delivery of health care services via clinics and hospitals resulted in the relative neglect of the MOH's traditional task of 'community watchdog' in respect to sources of danger to the people's health. As C. Webster has pointed out, the annual reports of the MOsH tended to become progress reports, listing the numbers of children inspected, dental caries filled and sanatorium beds provided.[6] It was left to others to investigate the effects of unemployment on health, and to bring to public notice the large number of cases of malnutrition in the depressed areas and the widespread morbidity among childbearing women.

Second, there was little to distinguish the services provided by public health doctors from those provided by GPs and voluntary hospitals. Indeed, during the inter-war years the salaried public health doctor was consistently accused of 'encroachment' by his private practitioner colleagues. Despite the uneven provision and often overlapping jurisdiction of local authority health services, MOsH were confident that any move towards 'state medicine' would inevitably strengthen their position, but their status within the medical profession was low and they were dependent on the BMA for support in salary negotiations. The BMA in its turn was determined to support the cause of the independent practitioner and to oppose salaried service. The Ministry of Health was not prepared either to take on the BMA or to favour local authority control over that of the voluntary hospitals. Thus it was to be expected that in 1946 salaried doctors would lose control of the clinics to the GPs, who remained independent contractors, and of the hospitals to a nationalized hospital service, which J.E. Pater has described as a 'simple and radical solution' to the conflict between local authority and voluntary hospital interests.[7]

PREVENTION, STATE MEDICINE AND 'ENCROACHMENT' IN THE 1920s

In 1919 the Consultative Council on Medical and Allied Services was asked to prepare a report on a scheme for the provision of medical services. The result, published less than twelve months later, was the Dawson Report,[8] popularly remembered on the one hand for its advocacy of health centres and its stress on the importance of positive health and 'physical culture', and on the other for its reluctance to face the crucial issues of payment for services by patients and terms and conditions for doctors. The Report argued that the changes it recommended were necessary because medicine was poorly organized and because it failed to bring new medical knowledge 'within reach of the people'.[9] The Report made the GP the key figure in its scheme for the delivery of medical services and argued for a system of medical organization based on the health centre that would end the GP's intellectual isolation and provide him access to laboratory and radiology services, operating rooms and a dispensary.

In the view of the Council:

Preventive and curative medicine cannot be separated on any sound principle, and in any scheme of medical services must be brought together in close coordination. They must likewise be both brought within the sphere of the GP, whose duties should embrace the work of communal as well as individual medicine. It appears that the present trend of the public health service towards the inclusion of certain special branches of curative work is tending to deprive both the medical student and the practitioner of the experience they need in these directions.[10]

Thus the Report advocated passing to the GP personal preventive services that were in the process of being developed by the local authorities and which had received a further impetus from the Maternal and Child Welfare Act 1918:

The GP, if adequately trained, should play a valuable part in the work of the communal services, e.g. ante-natal supervision, child welfare, both before and during school age, physical culture, tuberculosis, venereal disease.[11]

At the time the Council reported, these were the responsibility of the MOH. By implication, therefore, the Report confined the MOH to the environmental and sanitary duties that had characterized nineteenth-century public health work. Lord Dawson himself was both vehemently opposed to a state medical service and firmly committed to promoting the cause of the independent GP over and above that of the salaried public health doctor.[12]

The Dawson Report did not find favour at the Ministry, in part because its proposals left so many controversial issues open, particularly in respect to finance; partly because the Ministry experienced severe financial pressures soon after its publication; and partly because the Ministry did not share Dawson's extreme antipathy to the salaried medical officer.[13] Sir George Newman, chief medical officer at the newly formed Ministry of Health, never tired of emphasizing the importance of personal preventive medicine and the role of the public health department in educating the people in personal hygiene. Newman also paid tribute to the idea of the GP as the pivot of the medical system but clearly doubted that the majority of GPs were sufficiently trained in preventive medicine to take over the local authority clinic services.[14] Furthermore, in an article published in 1920, he showed that he was anxious to achieve the unified administration of poor law medicine, sanitation, school health, insurance and pensions under the local authorities, leaving open the question of the basis of payment of independent medical practitioners.[15]

Newman's beliefs regarding the essential principles of public health practice exercised a strong influence throughout the inter-war years. He insisted that:

We must give up the idea that health is comprised in sewerage, disinfection, the suppression of nuisances, the burial of the dead, notification and registration of disease, fever hospitals, and endless restrictive by-laws and regulations. Health springs from the domestic, social and personal life of the people.[16]

It was for this reason that he stressed the importance of the public health doctor's contact with individuals in order to provide health education. In his memorandum on the practice of preventive medicine, first issued in 1919, he argued for a new 'synthesis and integration' in medicine and, in particular, a closer integration between preventive and curative medicines.[17] He was quite prepared to acknowledge that 'the whole science and art of preventive medicine is . . . essentially clinical in origin and purpose' and he emphasized the importance of a clinical training for MOsH.[18] However, his conviction that the prevention of disease had become less a matter of removing external, environmental 'nuisances' and more a personal concern, brought the practice of public health very close to that of the GP.

The Times attacked Newman's ideas as 'socialistic' and favoured the proposals of the Dawson Report, much to the disgust of the editor of *Public Health*.[19] In all probability *The Times* exaggerated. The essence of Newman's thought was his commitment to the power of preventive medicine as health education, not a belief in state medicine. In 1925 he had advocated the education of working-class mothers as being the only way of bringing down the infant mortality rate, and he remained convinced that the decline in infant deaths was due to this cause alone.[20] Newman was ready to acknowledge the GP as the pivot of the medical service and anxious to see him practise preventive medicine too, doubting only that the medical curriculum of the 1920s provided him with enough knowledge to do so. Newman's personal faith in the MOH together with the fact that the public health departments provided the only coherent administrative framework for implementing the Ministry's initiatives during the inter-war years (the administration of national health insurance and the panel system being extremely complicated) help to explain why the Ministry preferred to continue to invest powers in the public health departments and to ignore the Dawson Report.

The reaction of public health doctors to the Dawson Report reflected the essential strength of their position. The editor of *Public Health* argued that the GP's knowledge of preventive medicine would not bear close inspection and that he was not in a position to administer the preventive medical services effectively.[21] In addition, public health doctors received public support for their clinic work. In 1919 the BMA instigated an inquiry into the role of the MOH and the GP in maternal and child welfare clinics. A committee of twelve (four of them MOsH) took evidence from a further ten persons and/or organizations.[22] The spokeswomen for the voluntary organizations involved in maternal and child welfare work were united in their preference for the whole-time medical officer, who could be relied on to do the work, and whose services were reportedly preferred by the mothers, over the part-time GP working on a rota. The evidence of the MOsH was measured and persuasive. None attacked the involvement of GPs. The statement of Dr J. Robertson, MOH for Birmingham, was typical: 'Preventive work is so important that I am anxious that every GP should take part'. But he continued: 'There is no inducement for him [the GP] at the present time to pay any attention to preventive medicine, and generally among the working classes, he fails so far as child welfare is concerned'.[23] Dr T. Shaddick Higgins, MOH for St Pancras, stressed that it made no difference whether an MOH or a GP staffed the infant welfare clinics as long as he was a specialist, but, as Dr Higgins pointed out, GPs learned little about infant care and management in the course of their training.[24] This was, of course, to assume that MOsH learned rather more, presumably while studying for the DPH. However, the General Medical Council's Resolutions and Rules for the DPH showed a heavy weighting in favour of instruction in bacteriology and sanitation throughout the inter-war years.[25]

In line with the burden of evidence presented to it, the BMA committee concluded that GPs taking on clinic duties needed to have a real knowledge of and interest in the work. It endorsed the value of the work done by the public health departments in the field of maternal and child welfare but cautioned that they should confine themselves to truly preventive and advisory services:

The promoters of some Centres . . . by means of solicitation by Home Visitors and by generous gifts of milk etc., have tried to teach expectant mothers that the Centres are the places to which they should go and should take their babies for medical advice and treatment.[26]

This was felt to be unfair to the independent practitioner. Certainly from the public's point of view, there is evidence that a visit to the clinic was seen as a welcome alternative to incurring a GP's bill.[27] Nevertheless, this committee of the BMA, which supported the cause of the independent GP over the salaried MO,[28] was forced to admit that in the main GPs were both unwilling and unable to do the kind of personal preventive medical work that the public health departments had made a central component of their activities.

Thus throughout the 1920s public health departments were able to sustain their claim that 'public health work is mainly clinical medicine but clinical medicine of a special kind'.[29] In this they were following the principles set out by Newman, but the distinction between the clinical work of the public health department and of the GP rested on the difference between the provision of prevention and advice on the one hand and treatment on the other. Evidence suggests that public health departments were, in fact, careful not to offer any treatment other than for the mildest ailments,[30] but the boundary between the two types of provision was obviously hard to draw. Furthermore, philosophically, public health had painted itself into a rather narrow corner that was hard to distinguish from curative medicine.

In 1927 the issue of 'encroachment' by the public health service into the territory of the private practitioner was once more on the agenda of the BMA's Annual Representative Meeting. One resolution referred to the 'insidious inroads continually being made on private medical practice under the auspices of the state, voluntary bodies and others'.[31] Dr A. Cox the secretary of the BMA, was asked to investigate and he reported in 1928. While favouring the cause of the GP, he argued judiciously that 'we would be doing a great service to the profession if we educated them [GPs] to claim and to take their part in the present scheme, instead of bemoaning the encroachments on private practice'.[32] Cox pointed out that the local authority services for mothers, infants and school children had grown out of the Medical Inspection of School Children Act 1907, which the BMA had supported, and that the Ministry, and in particular Newman, had never denied the importance of the role played by the GP in the medical services.

Cox observed local authority work in six areas and concluded that 'few private practitioners . . . have any first hand knowledge of the procedure. I was astounded, on asking the doctors I met at various meetings to find that hardly any had ever been inside one of these centres'.[33] In short, GPs had shown little inclination to do work that all were agreed should be done. In every area he visited Cox was impressed by the genuine attempt that was made to get the patient to consult a private doctor before giving anything except treatment for very minor ailments. Cox limited his recommendations to a plea that MOsH should employ more part-time GPs in clinics in order to enlist the GP in the cause of preventive medicine and to promote harmony in the profession.

However, the BMA's Committee on Encroachments on the Sphere of Private Practice by the Activities of Local Authorities, to which Cox passed his report, took a much firmer line. In its Interim Report, issued in 1928, the Committee urged private practitioners not to allow personal preventive work 'to pass without protest' to local authority doctors.[34] Its Final Report stated firmly that medical practice with individuals, whether sick or requiring knowledge on how to maintain their health, 'naturally belongs to, because it is best provided by, private practitioners'.[35] The Committee claimed that the private GP had a wider range of clinical experience and a more direct knowledge of home conditions than the medical officer. It concluded by recommending a complete separation between the work of GPs and MOsH in much the same manner as the Dawson Report: 'The main sphere of the private practitioner is the giving of medical advice and treatment to individuals; the main sphere of the public health medical officer is the promotion of healthy conditions for the community'.[36] While stressing that the MOH and the GP should take an interest in each other's work, the Committee recommended that public health doctors should not undertake any clinical work that could be done by a GP. This amounted to a direct refutation by the BMA of public health's claim to be doing a special kind of clinical medicine, or 'applied physiology', as the *Medical Officer* called it in 1930.[37]

The response from public health doctors was muted. The *Medical Officer* published an angry editorial in which it argued that the term 'encroachment' was incorrect; local authorities were merely undertaking work in fields that the GP failed to occupy.[38] It also disputed the idea that only GPs possessed enough knowledge about the family situation of the individual to undertake preventive work and defended the employment of full-time medical officers in clinics. Nevertheless, the journal ended by endorsing the ideas that GPs should do clinic work where possible. In fact, MOsH did not have to be overly defensive. As the *Medical Officer* pointed out, so-called encroachment was sanctioned by law.[39] Indeed, in 1929 MOsH were preoccupied with the implications of the Local Government Act, which further enlarged their empire by giving them control over what had been the poor law hospitals, and to which they preferred to appoint consultants rather than GPs.[40] Dr Buchan, the MOH for Willesden, where the wide range of personal medical services provided by the local authority had roused particular ire among GPs, was led to remark that 'the very large provisions and concentrations in respect of public health and medical work made by the Local Government Act of 1929, are likely to lead to a State Medical Service'.[41]

Despite this further consolidation of the position of public health departments, the status of the MOH remained low within the medical profession and, paradoxically, MOsH were reliant on the support of the BMA in respect to salary negotiations. In 1923 the BMA and the Society of Medical Officers of Health agreed on a scheme of co-operation whereby the BMA agreed to support a minimum salary scale for public health doctors, and both organizations altered their constitutions to allow direct representation by the other on their respective governing bodies.[42] In return the Society of Medical Officers of Health agreed that it would not act independently on medico-political matters. The agreement was welcomed by the *Medical Officer* as promoting harmony in the profession,[43] but it undoubtedly helped to stifle the voice of the public health doctor. The agreement was renegotiated periodically during the 1920s and 1930s, but its terms continued to be controversial. One MOH wrote in outrage that the Society had 'been sold body and soul to the British Medical Association'.[44] MOsH in the East Midland Branch of the Society observed correctly that the BMA did not see fit to consult the Society in framing its views on 'A General Medical Service for the Nation', published in 1937, which again promoted the cause of the independent GP at the expense of the salaried medical officer.[45]

Yet in 1929, the same year as the publication of the Committee on Encroachment's Report, the Society of Medical Officers of Health had reason to be grateful to the BMA for negotiating a salary scale with local authorities. Salaries had previously been fixed at the discretion of the local government employers. The Local Government Act 1929 at last obliged rather than permitted all county authorities to employ a full-time MOH, which necessitated a substantial reorganization of public health work and involved substantially increased costs for local authorities. The negotiations between the BMA and the Society of Medical Officers of Health on one side, and the County Council Association, the Association of Municipal Corporations, the Urban District Councils Association, the Rural District Councils Association, the Association of Education Committees and the Mental Hospitals Association on the other, were complex. Sir Percy Jackson, head of the County Council Association, argued strongly that assistant medical officers should be paid only £400 a year on a par with civil servants in the Education Offices, who had, as he put it, 'degrees from the old universities'.[46] Another local authority representative suggested that public health work might be regarded as a stepping-stone to specialist work in private practice. But Sir Robert Bolam of the BMA cut in fairly to say that 'in the great majority of instances it [public health work] is a disablement for further work in the profession in the open market'.[47]

MOsH relied on the BMA in 1929 and in subsequent negotiations to argue for parity with doctors in other parts of the profession. The BMA asked for a £600 minimum salary, and under the Askwith scale agreed upon in 1929 MOsH actually got a minimum of £500. Throughout the 1930s MOsH continued to experience problems with local authorities advertising posts below the scale.[48] In addition, by the late 1930s there was a serious promotion block in the public health service;[49] in a rapidly expanding service, senior appointments had become too few in number. Furthermore Professors W.W.

Jameson and R.M.F. Picken reported to the Society of Medical Officers of Health in 1936 that senior appointments were left 'too much to chance', by which they meant that lay members of local authorities did not always appoint the best-qualified candidate.[50]

'COMMUNITY WATCHDOG'? PUBLIC HEALTH IN THE 1930s

During the 1930s the definition of public health as clinical work of a different order from that done by the GP was diluted by the public health doctor's involvement in hospital administration. Public health's sphere of influence grew substantially but with little philosophical underpinning. Indeed, the vast majority of public health doctors were outstripped in terms of both their thinking about health and in the performance of their traditional role of community watchdog by a number of pressure groups, social scientists and a few more socially aware specialists within the medical profession. Nevertheless, because of the ever-broadening scope of their responsibilities, MOsH remained convinced that state medicine and their own influence would continue to grow.

The major preoccupation of MOsH during the 1930s was undoubtedly their new administrative responsibilities for the hospitals, although it should be remembered that local authority takeover of poor law medical institutions was slow and that as late as 1939 50 per cent of general hospital beds remained under the control of the poor law. In 1933 Dr C.O. Stallybrass, MOH for Liverpool, provided a detailed account of how Liverpool had appropriated two poor law hospitals under the Local Government Act 1929 and of the extensive planning and the extra staff that had been needed in order to reform their administration.[51] In an influential article published a few years later, Dr A. Massey, MOH for Coventry, emphasized the importance of medical as opposed to lay administration within the hospital.[52] (The importance of medical administration continued to be an important theme during the 1950s and 1960s, when it became necessary to justify medical control of a wide range of domiciliary services.)

Fears were expressed that the work of hospital administration diverted the MOH from his main task of prevention. The *Medical Officer*, in particular, warned that the MOH was neglecting the work of 'individual prevention', still in its infancy according to the president of the Society of Medical Officers of Health, in favour of 'pathology'.[53] At the Public Health Congress of 1930 Sir Arthur Newsholme, who had been the chief medical officer to the Local Government Board prior to the First World War, suggested that the work of co-ordinating the medical services was an inevitable result of the 1929 Act but would prove a temporary phenomenon.[54] But the editor of the *Medical Officer* wondered, more realistically perhaps, whether MOsH would be able easily to return 'from the pursuit of pathology to their proper allegiance to physiology;[55] commenting crossly: 'Much recent public health work seems to aim at converting it into a gigantic hospital.'[56] The *Medical Officer* insisted that while the responsibilities of the public health department encompassed sanitation, treatment and administration as well as prevention, the MOH should devote most of his time to the latter. Clearly, prevention was still being defined after the manner of Newman. As late as 1937 the journal reiterated that 90 per cent of the medical officer's job was clinical, but in the sense of 'applied physiology' rather than the provision of treatment.[57]

There is no evidence that the philosophy of public health developed further in the 1930s or that the *Medical Officer's* concern regarding MOsH's hospital responsibilities was widely shared. Little on this theme surfaced in *Public Health* and at least one MOH produced a spirited defence of the MOH's involvement in hospitals as being very much a part of preventive work:

I understand there is a common belief that MOsH, during recent years have devoted so much time to the development of the growing municipal hospital schemes that they have become divorced from the practice of preventive medicine. If it is correct to define preventive medicine as including all measures devised to prevent premature death and to maintain optimum health I suggest that the development of the municipal hospital services represents a development of preventive medicine almost as revolutionary as the growth of the maternal and child welfare services and of the school medical service in the early part of this century and that of the sanitary services in the latter part of the last century.[58]

Thus prevention was redefined *ex post facto* to accommodate the burgeoning concerns of the MOH, providing the GP with some justification for regarding public health and preventive medicine as being merely synonymous with state medicine.

Thoughtful commentators on the trend in public health work were few, but Dr W.G. Savage, MOH for Somerset, subjected the field to a wide-ranging criticism in 1935.[59] He began by deploring the effects of the 1929 Act: 'We have become administrators of beds largely occupied by the end products of disease and supervisors of defectives; in a word, largely enmeshed in functions which are not our proper business.' But Savage went further than this, condemning also the clinical work that absorbed so much of the medical officer's time as dull and routine and calling for more epidemiological research. He felt that the ever-increasing range of responsibilities invested in the MOH by the Ministry had served only to hold up progress in preventive medicine and, with considerable astuteness, pointed to the isolation hospitals as an example. Vast sums had been spent on these and MOsH were more concerned with their administration than with putting into practice the kind of modern medical knowledge that rendered them unnecessary.

The history of diphtheria immunization serves to illustrate Savage's point. The responsibility for immunization rested very much with individual local authorities and the local MOH, whose task it was to persuade his local public health committee to pursue an active immunization campaign. This often required special persistence in the financially straitened circumstances of the 1930s. Effective immunization agents were available by the early 1920s, and reports of successful, large-scale trials in Canada and the USA were published at the end of the decade. Yet between 1927 and 1930 the medical journals show that large numbers of MOsH were preoccupied with more traditional approaches to the control of the disease and were deeply distrustful of immunization. A significant number seem to have concentrated their efforts on swabbing throats (and sometimes noses) in an effort to identify carriers and on confining victims in isolation hospitals.[60] L. Bryder's recent work on TB has found a similar tendency among public health doctors employed as tuberculosis officers to identify with the institutional treatment of the disease.[61] In the case of immunization, some MOsH believed that complete immuniza-tion gave a false sense of security and that as long as under 50 per cent remained unimmunized, the mixture of protected and unprotected not only did little to prevent the spread of the disease but also added materially to the difficulty of detecting it and of limiting its course. C. Killick Millard, the MOH for Leicester and a strong supporter of sterilization and euthan-asia, rehearsed the full gamut of dubious epidemiological arguments against diphtheria immunization in a memo for his public health committee as late as 1935.[62] Deaths from the disease in Ontario, Canada, had been reduced from 25.7 per 1,000 in 1920 to 0.9 in 1939, but in Britain the rate showed no decline until 1941 when a national immunization scheme was eventually implemented.

Looking back in 1939, R.M.F. Picken, professor of preventive medicine at the Welsh School of Medicine, felt that the MOH had taken on too much administrative work to be an effective proponent of preventive medicine:

Public health might have developed on very different lines. It might well have remained purely preventive, grown out of sanitation to be concerned mainly with the problems of the nutrition of the people, their physical fitness, and public education generally, and kept away from any sort of medical advice and treatment of the individual . . . we have moved a long way in quite a different direction. I think, for instance, that one of the reasons why the United States of America has been far more successful in diphtheria immunisation then we have is that their public health departments have not been burdened with the great variety of medical work with which we have been saddled . . . .[63]

Picken was convinced that MOsH had strayed from their proper sphere of work and had indeed been guilty of encroachment. As both Picken and Savage recognized, MOsH had been diverted in particular by their responsibilities for institutional treatment, in municipal hospitals, TB sanatoria, isolation and mental hospitals. Ever-increasing efforts were made, for example, to classify the 'mentally defective', carried out against a background of eugenic propaganda about a deterioration in the 'national intelligence'.[64] By 1939, 130,000 mental patients were in institutions.

The evidence suggests that MOsH neglected many aspects of their duties as community watchdogs during the 1930s, in respect both to more traditional areas such as immunization and to the new-found concerns over the effects of long-term unemployment on nutritional standards and levels of morbidity and mortality. In large part this neglect may be attributed to the narrow conception of public health as medical service and administration that characterized the thinking of the MOsH during the 1930s. In addition, many local authorities resisted any call for new items of expenditure on financial grounds, although, in the case of diphtheria, immunization would certainly have proved less costly than isolation in hospital. Similarly the Ministry of Health strongly resisted any implication that a further injection of funds was required to stop deterioration of the nation's health.

For the most part the optimistic annual reports filed by MOsH sought to assure the public and the Ministry that the nation's health was well maintained. The Ministry consistently refuted evidence provided by pressure groups and social scientists as to the existence of a relationship between high unemployment and deteriorating health standards, reserving particular condemnation for the handful of MOsH who expressed similar opinions. Dr J.J. Butterworth, MOH for Lancashire, was consistently optimistic in his conclusions despite the high infant mortality rate, and in Cumberland, Dr K. Fraser concluded that there was 'really very little malnutrition ... due to actual lack of food—there are a number of poorly nourished-looking children; but in nearly all of them it is a case of poor general physique rather than malnutrition'.[65] Some fifty authorities, mainly in the depressed areas, sent in returns to the Ministry of Health suggesting that they were experiencing less than half the average incidence of subnormal nutrition.[66] Local MOsH relied mainly on visual assessment, and as the Children's Minimum Council (a pressure group allied closely to the campaign for family allowances) pointed out, the result was a collection of personal observations. M. Green, the secretary of the Council, quoted the case of two medical officers who made successive examinations of the same group of children at an interval of seven days. The doctors' assessments differed at the first examination, and both

changed their opinions at the second.[67] The *Medical Officer*
responded to the publication of Green's results with a singular
lack of enthusiasm, supposing it meant that 'we must put in our
perennial plea for milk and herrings'.[68] Many local authorities
supplied very few school meals and did very little preventive
dentistry or ante-natal and post-natal care; and some MOsH,
like Dr W. Frazer in Liverpool, were philosophically opposed
to giving nutritional supplements.[69] In adopting an optimistic
view, MOsH were undoubtedly telling the Ministry of Health
what it wanted to hear.

The lead in raising questions concerning the health status of
the population during the 1930s was taken first by political
lobby groups such as the Children's Minimum Council, the
Committee against Malnutrition and the National Unemployed Workers Movement, all of which called for a higher
level of unemployment benefit to enable families to secure the
minimum nutritional requirements set out by the BMA.
Second, 'amateur' and 'professional' social scientists took the
lead in investigating the incidence of malnutrition, morbidity
and mortality in the population. The Women's Health Inquiry
surveyed the health status of some 1,250 working-class wives
and found that only 31.3 per cent could be considered to be in
'good health', 22.3 per cent were categorized as 'indifferent',
15.2 per cent as 'bad', and 31.2 per cent as 'very grave'.[70] The
Women's Group on Public Welfare's survey of the conditions
of children evacuated from the town at the beginning of the war
painted a similarly black picture.[71] R. Titmuss also undertook
a survey of the wastage of infant life in relation to socio-
economic class and concluded correctly that the decline in the
overall infant mortality rate was not matched by a narrowing
of the gap between social classes.[72] Third, a smaller number of
medical specialists, particularly obstetricians and gynaecolo-
gists, attempted to draw attention to the large amount of
maternal mortality and morbidity. Sir James Young estimated
that 'about 60% of hospital gynaecology is a legacy from
vitiated childbearing'.[73] He despaired of 'the apathy of
organized medicine towards the positive value of health ideals',
and the profession's 'devotion to disease [which] has blinded us
to the duties of health'.[74]

Dr G.C.M. McGonigle was one of the very few MOsH who

attempted both to conceptualize public health more in terms of positive health than preventive clinical medicine, and, more exceptionally still, to investigate actively the health status of his population along the lines pursued in the main by non-medically trained groups and individuals. In 1920 McGonigle referred to the importance of 'understanding the normal biology of the human being' and of getting away from 'the conception of our science as being preventive medicine, and visualize it as the science of maintaining normality'.[75] In many respects, this echoed the philosophy of the pioneer Peckham Health Centre, opened in 1926. The Centre was alone in the 1930s in developing a philosophy of health, as distinct from the practice of medicine and delivery of medical services. The Centre's non-medical founders, G.S. Williamson and I. Pearse, believed that the cultivation of health required a completely different approach from the cure of disease and that the study of health derived from biological rather than pathological principles. The key to health promotion, they argued, lay in the relation between the human being and his or her environment (particularly the home and the family) and in the study of the normal. When Pearse started work in an infant welfare centre in London's East End after World War I, she complained that she had to do so without ever having seen a healthy baby.[76]

For his part McGonigle was virtually alone among public health doctors in insisting that the general decline in infant mortality began long before the advent of child welfare work[77] and thereby questioned the value of what the *Medical Officer* had dubbed 'applied physiology'. He called rather for the kind of research Savage had hinted at, a large-scale investigation of the incidence of defects in young children and their causes, and went on to plead for 'intensive study of normal biology'. McGonigle was also one of the few MOsH who proved immediately receptive to the ideas of social medicine in the 1940s. In his own district of Stockton-on-Tees, he undertook an influential study of a group of families who were moved from slum houses to a new housing estate and showed that their health status deteriorated relative to those who stayed behind, largely because a greater proportion of their income was absorbed by the higher rents that were charged on the new estate.[78] McGonigle's definition of public health's task as being concerned above all with the determinants of health and their promotion was far in advance of that of the vast majority of his colleagues.

Furthermore, it was a definition that inevitably caused him to touch on sensitive political issues. By confining themselves to clinic work and hospital administration most public health doctors managed to avoid controversy. The Ministry of Health dismissed McGonigle's efforts as those of 'a promising Labour politician'.[79] Likewise the Ministry could not countenance the evidence of malnutrition provided by social investigators without also admitting the justice of the case presented by various lobby groups for raising unemployment benefit. The Nutrition Advisory Committee, established by the Ministry in 1931, set much lower standards of nutrition than did a report issued by the BMA. The Ministry stuck firmly by its report and circulated its results regarding the daily intake of protein and numbers of calories necessary to maintain good nutrition, to the local authorities.[80] Any dissenters, such as McGonigle, were upbraided. Newman's belief that the essential role of public health lay in the provision of personal advice came through strongly in his call for public health departments to undertake more education in nutrition. The Ministry's Nutrition Advisory Committee hired Dr E. Nash, MOH for Isleworth and Heston, to give cookery demonstrations to housewives on low incomes.[81]

Similarly, Newman was prepared to admit privately that the Ministry could not respond to calls from groups such as the Women's Health Inquiry and obstetricians such as Sir James Young to investigate the high incidence of morbidity among childbearing women for fear that such an investigation 'could have but one ending, namely, the demonstration of a great mass of sickness and impairment attributable to childbirth, which would create a demand for organized treatment by the state'.[82] For all Newman's willingness to add in an *ad hoc* manner to the powers of local authorities, he was not prepared to argue that the balance of medical care provision should be swung in favour of a state service.

Yet this was what MOsH, deeply involved in their expanding medical services, expected. The Society of Medical Officers of Health confidently predicted that public health doctors would increasingly control the medical services.[83] Dr C. Thompson, MOH for Belfast, gave his opinion that 'the days of individualism in medicine have to a definite extent passed away and that we have passed and are increasingly passing into a semi-state system of medical practice'.[84] However, the BMA's scheme for a *General Medical Service for the Nation*, published in 1938, while proposing that medical services 'should be directed to the achievement of positive health and the prevention of disease no less than to the relief of sickness',[85] recommended firmly in favour of extending national health insurance in order to bring such a service within the reach of every family. Like the Dawson Report, the BMA document envisaged making the GP the lynch-pin of the medical service and of providing him with laboratory services and access to consultants and specialists, although the concept of the health centre was not mentioned.

Dr C. Hill, deputy secretary of the BMA, addressed members of the Society of Medical Officers of Health about the BMA's proposals early in 1937. He charged that local authorities had continued to reject the opportunities of using GPs' services, preferring 'an effective extension of their own activities regardless of the continuity of the medical care of the sick person'. Dr M. Radford, MOH for St Pancras, challenged Hill's views and stated his belief that it would be impossible to provide a full preventive and curative service along the lines of the BMA document without moving to a full salaried state medical service. For only then would the problem of encroachment cease to exist.[86]

In fact, a virtual impasse had been reached. As C. Webster's research has revealed, the Ministry showed no more inclination to develop national health insurance in the late 1930s than to plump for the fully-fledged salaried state service the public health doctors wanted.[87] Indeed some semblance of balance between the two views would be perpetuated through the tripartite medical service that emerged in 1946, albeit that public health's empire crumbled under the weight of opposition from both the BMA and the voluntary hospitals.

THE DIMINUTION OF PUBLIC HEALTH IN THE 1940s

Social medicine and public health
Defining social medicine
The term 'social medicine' was not widely used until 1942. Its roots were to be found in the work of social investigators and pressure groups on health status and the determinants of health during the 1930s. J. Ryle, Regius professor of physics at Cambridge, who accepted the invitation to become the first professor of social medicine at Oxford in 1942, paid tribute to the work of the Peckham Health Centre and the Women's Group on Public Welfare.[88] However, it is doubtful whether the concept of social medicine would have found concrete expression had it not been for the committed discussion of health planning and reconstruction during the war.

In a 1940 address to medical students at Cambridge, Ryle counselled:

By one means or another you must develop the social conscience, which has in the view of many of us, been too little evident in years preceding the war ... medical students and doctors as a body . . . have held themselves too much aloof from the larger social problems . . . . I do not ask you necessarily to ally yourself with any particular creed, but I do ask you to be seriously interested in man's environment and the possibilities for its improvement.[89]

He addressed his audience passionately and told them that he wished he could take them to the East End of London to see for themselves the 'disgraceful' housing conditions of the poor which militated against health.

Until recently, the dominant view of social policy-making during World War II, derived from Titmuss's official history of the period,[90] has stressed the importance of the social consensus and social conscience that were produced by the war. However, J. Macnicol has concluded that reform engineered consensus rather than vice versa: 'The exaggerated rhetoric with which the reforms were packaged achieved its objective of engineering consent and minimising social upheaval'.[91] Social medicine was part of a social awakening among an academic and policy-making élite that may well have encouraged Titmuss in his optimistic view of the wartime policy-making process. It is certainly interesting to find that he played a strong role in developing the concept of social medicine. In 1942 he drafted a paper explaining the idea:

The flow of reconstruction reports, both medical and lay, are symptomatic of a new approach to Social Freedom. In reconstruction, social medicine, by that name or another, will be called upon for much. The establishment of the Institute of Social Medicine measures yet another stage in the growing recognition of the social relations of Health. Our vision is broadening; men are being pictured against a man-made environment; the multiple factor in disease and disorder is replacing the single causation concept; *the study of life is replacing a morbid concentration on death*. The emergence of what we now call social medicine has been a long and faltering journey. The catalyst of a world-wide civil war, and even more a new concept of peace, have quickened the process.[92]

In Titmuss's view the planning of health and social services were intimately linked and both were to be developed in response to human needs. Furthermore, in the context of wartime medical and social planning this was by no means a minority view. The Interim Report of the Medical Planning Commission, inspired by the BMA and comprising seventy-three representatives of professional bodies, showed that during wartime the medical profession was prepared to relax its insistence on non-salaried autonomous practice in favour of group practice in health centres, with the GPs who worked there being paid in part by salary and in part by capitation.[93] However, as Honigsbaum has pointed out, the profession's radicalism was deceptive in that a major motivating force behind the report was the desire to contain a menace of the local authority clinic.[94] Medical Planning Research, a larger group of 200 much younger members of the BMA, went still further, addressing the relationship between poverty, environmental planning and health, and calling for a single social security contribution and a National Health Corporation as the basis for the organization of post-war social and health services.[95] Indeed, during these early years of the war, the concept of social medicine was often confused with state medicine and the emerging plans for a National Health Service, despite the efforts of academics to define it in terms of the philosophy and practice of medicine. In welcoming the establishment of the Institute of Social Medicine at Oxford, Sir

Wilson Jameson, the chief medical officer, saw fit to trace the effect of war on social medicine, by which he clearly meant the collective provision of medical services.[96] Similarly, the editor of the *Lancet* welcomed the Beveridge Report as the 'culmination of 100 years of social medicine beginning with Chadwick'.[97]

However, after the establishment of the Oxford chair in 1942, the development of social medicine was conditioned by its location within the universities and, in the search for academic credibility, it moved further away from a concern with health policy and social science. Thus social medicine failed in two crucial respects to fulfil its early promise. In part because of this and in part because of their own narrowness of vision, public health practitioners did not take up the idea of social medicine. This in turn resulted in a damaging rift between the teachers and practitioners of public health.

The chair at Oxford was endowed by the Nuffield Provincial Hospitals Trust. In an article about the place of social medicine in medical reconstruction published in 1942, Sir Farquhar Buzzard, who actively supported the setting up of the new department at Oxford, stressed the need for more research on the promotion of health and the prevention of disease. He envisaged the new Oxford Institute and other similar centres of social medicine promoting research in these two areas and reorienting the whole focus of the medical curriculum.[98]

From the first, the concerns of social medicine were defined primarily by academics. Ryle followed Buzzard with a letter to the *BMJ* in which he attempted to flesh out his definition of social medicine as 'applied aetiology':

Social medicine is clinical medicine activated in its aetiological inquiries by social conscience as well as scientific interest and having as its main purpose the education of progressive and lay thought and the direction of legislation on behalf of national health and efficiency.[99]

This was Ryle's first attempt at a definition of social medicine and it neatly encapsulated the two most important building blocks of his thinking on the subject, the importance of social conscience and a commitment to clinical medicine. It seems that by the late 1940s the latter had become the more important strand, but in 1942 he continued to emphasize that medicine must change its focus and concerns. In an address to student members of the BMA he talked of 'the obligations of medicine' and the need for a new 'more human' medicine, saying that 'doctors . . . have been too little cooperative, too individualistic both in their own affairs and in their way of regarding diseases and patients'.[100]

Two sympathizers attempted to modify Ryle's preliminary definition of social medicine. Sir Robert McCarrison, whose work on nutrition and advocacy of whole foods had been a great influence on the founders of the Peckham Health Centre, asked for the word 'clinical' to be omitted. To this Ryle replied that one of his aims was to reform the way clinicians studied aetiology to include social and environmental factors. C. McNeil, professor of paediatrics at Edinburgh, preferred the older term 'applied physiology' to 'applied aetiology', but to this Ryle responded that physiology was about function and aetiology was about cause and the study of the latter was crucial to establish the conditions necessary for good health.[101]

In a longer article on the meaning of social medicine, published the following year, Ryle took as one of his main themes the extent to which social medicine envisaged something far more comprehensive than preventive medicine. As 'a direct development and expansion of clinical medicine', he argued that social medicine embodied the

idea of medicine applied to the service of man as *socius*, as fellow or comrade, with a view to a better understanding and more durable assistance of all his main and contributory troubles which are inimical to active health and not merely removing or alleviating a present pathology. It embodies also the idea of medicine applied in the service of *societas*, or the community of men, with a view to lowering the incidence of all preventable disease and raising the general level of human fitness.[102]

Ryle's determination to link social medicine firmly to clinical medicine was paralleled by his second main theme, that social medicine had no immediate concern with medical or other politics.

Nevertheless, the concept of social medicine remained vague. There was broad agreement only that social medicine should investigate the influence of social, environmental and genetic factors on the incidence of disease and identify and promote factors favourable to the health of the people. F.A.E. Crewe, professor of social medicine at Edinburgh University, summarized the concerns of social medicine as 'the definition of the social environment in relation to the prevalence of morbidity and mortality . . . [and] . . . the social agencies which are propitious to maximizing health in the widest sense of the word'.[103] In his view it was the latter above all that distinguished social medicine from preventive medicine and public health. With his background in genetics, Crewe was very anxious to develop a 'social biology'. Looking back in 1949, he was convinced that the theoretical exposition of social medicine was not as well developed as had been the much earlier concept of social hygiene in the work of the German, A. Grotjahn.[104] He was supported in this view by Major A. Greenwood, a leading medical statistician, and G. Rosen, an American observer, neither of whom could see that Ryle's definition of social medicine had gone beyond Grotjahn's concept of social hygiene in any significant respect.[105]

Increasingly, the concept of social medicine was narrowed in order to stake a claim to academic respectability. Ryle's own work increasingly emphasized not only the links with clinical medicine and epidemiology at the expense of social science and health policy, but also the importance of the study of 'social pathology'—the quantity and cause of disease—at the expense of the more radical and difficult aim of promoting health.[106] Crewe also stressed that the essence of social medicine was the science of epidemiology, and L. Hogben, professor of social medicine at Birmingham, described social medicine as being concerned with medical statistics, albeit of health as well as disease.[107] As D. Armstrong has pointed out, the social survey was the basic tool of social medicine, and its development in twentieth-century social science research was crucial to the development of the concept of social medicine.[108]

The difference of opinion between both Ryle and the MRC on the one hand, and J.N. Morris and R. Titmuss on the other, serves to highlight the changing emphasis of social medicine in the universities. Morris, an epidemiologist, had met Titmuss in connection with the latter's work on infant mortality in the 1930s. Both attached considerable importance to the use of social science as well as epidemiology in the study of factors inimical and favourable to health, and to the study of health policy.[109] In the case of their commitment to social science they found themselves at odds with Ryle's increasing concern to steer social medicine clear of controversy, something that was difficult to do if full consideration was to be given to social and environmental variables. In 1943 Morris and Titmuss sent their work on the epidemiology of rheumatic heart disease[110] to Ryle, who commented that 'painstaking and valuable though the enquiry has been it seems to protest the poverty factor too much and your other contributions bearing on social medicine have been so valuable that it would be a pity to risk drawing adverse criticism in respect of a very important social disease'.[111] A month later Ryle wrote privately to Dr C.O. Stallybrass, the MOH for Liverpool, to thank him for sending a copy of his address to social workers in Liverpool and commented that it was 'a rather sad reflection that we [have] had to invoke their aid (partly) in order to re-humanize our medicine'.[112] However, in regard to its public image, Ryle was concerned that social medicine build up its reputation as a scientific and necessarily apolitical field of study.

Morris and Titmuss persuaded the MRC to set up a social medicine unit, which was established at the Central Middlesex Hospital in 1948. But they encountered opposition from the MRC over the research programme for the unit. One of their proposals involved a thorough investigation of health services in Willesden (the borough in which the Central Middlesex Hospital was located), but this was vetoed by the MRC as work essential to the Ministry of Health, but 'not in the nature of research at all'. Sir Edward Mellanby, on behalf of the MRC, advised Morris to 'find simple problems which you can tackle without all the paraphernalia of semi-digested information that a survey of this kind would provide',[113] to which Morris replied tartly, 'I am afraid that we have yet to come across any social problems that are simple'.[114] The MRC obviously did not regard the study of health policy as legitimate medical research.

The Oxford Institute carried out inquiries into the incidence of peptic ulcer in industry and of fluorosis in a local population, and into the effect of adding potassium iodide to the vitamin A and D tablets issued to expectant mothers.[115] An

American observer remarked astutely in 1951 that the Institute concerned itself more and more with factors affecting mortality and morbidity, shying away from both 'the allegedly sentimental aspects of social medicine . . . often stigmatized as the "unmarried mother" category of social problems' as well as organizational and operational problems of the health services.[116] In Oxford and in Birmingham social medicine increasingly came to mean medical statistics. In 1953 Sidney Leff went further still, charging that academic practitioners of social medicine tended to collect data 'merely to find correlations'. Leff was right in his perception that social medicine lacked direction and that one of its main weaknesses lay in the arbitrary selection of problems for study which were often unrelated to the practice of medicine or to the life of the community.[117]

MOsH and social medicine

Proponents of social medicine took considerable pains to differentiate the new subject from the concept of preventive medicine and 'applied physiology', and the practice of public health. Ryle argued that social medicine extended the interests of public health and altered its emphasis. Whereas public health was concerned primarily with environmental and personal health services, social medicine derived its inspiration from clinical experience and tried to study man in relation to all aspects of his nature and nurture. Second, while public health was preoccupied with infectious disease, social medicine was concerned with the epidemiology of all prevalent diseases. And finally, social medicine took within its province the whole work of medical sociology, defined by Ryle as the work of social diagnosis and the aftercare services provided by the hospital almoner (social worker).[118] In an address to the West of England Branch of the Society of Medical Officers of Health, W. Hobson, professor of social and industrial medicine at the University of Sheffield, stressed that social medicine attempted to link clinical and preventive medicine. Public health was more limited in its scope, primarily because there were many factors affecting health not encompassed by the Public Health Acts. Hobson emphasized above all the need for research on medical statistics.[119]

Most academicians were convinced that the public health

departments were old-fashioned in their approach. In his address, Hobson commented on the 'woeful lack of data on which to base a scientific approach to the planning of health services and an absence of any kind of research organization in public health departments'.[120] In his inaugural address he made his position clearer still, declaring social medicine to be:

a philosophy which should permeate all branches of medicine and as a university discipline, its teaching and research should be on a wide and fundamental basis. Its activities should be governed by the search for knowledge for its own sake and not necessarily for any local practical reasons. Public health on the other hand, is the practical application of the principles of social medicine to the benefit of the community as a whole.[121]

In many ways the response of public health doctors was predictable. In 1942 the concept of social medicine was greeted with considerable enthusiasm. This changed to perplexity when the concept remained vaguely defined and finally to outright rejection by the vast majority of public health doctors and by the public health journals. They were probably wrong in dismissing social medicine as 'nothing new', but their impatience with the discipline's high academic tone and its reluctance to consider practical questions concerning the health services was understandable.

In 1942 the *Medical Officer* gave 'wholehearted support' to Sir Farquhar Buzzard's call for the establishment of social medicine research centres, commenting that 'it would be strange if we did not, for we have called repeatedly for the same thing, the study of preventive medicine to settle the fundamental problem of health—"Why Smith is a victim and Jones escapes" '.[122] Thus at the outset the journal read social medicine as a valuable source of support in the campaign for preventive medicine. When the aims of the Oxford Institute were published, the journal was disappointed, however:

We read it [social medicine] . . . to embrace something at present loose and relate it to the science already pursued to found a system of communal health dependent upon factors other than the known, or about to be discovered, specific causes of differential diseases.[123]

The editor could see little difference between the aims of the

Institute and those of the London School of Hygiene. Writing in *Public Health*, the MOH for Lincolnshire was also puzzled. He found it easy enough to endorse the Oxford Institute's first aim, 'the investigation of the influence of social, genetic, environmental and domestic factors on disease and disability', but he found the second aim, 'to seek and promote measures for the protection of the individual and of the community against such forces as interfere with the full development and maintenance of man's mental and physical capacity' so all-encompassing as to be meaningless. He also found it 'difficult to escape the feeling that many powerful and influential medical men still think of MOsH as drain inspectors'.[124] Only a very few MOsH embraced the ideas of social medicine. J. Kershaw, the MOH for Accrington, was one, seeing social medicine as 'the development of medicine in relation to social life'. However, he also noted that 'the biggest danger' facing the new specialty was that it might become too academic.[125]

In 1945 the Society of Medical Officers of Health held their Annual General Meeting at the Oxford Institute and Ryle spoke to them of the need for co-operation between academic and practitioners.[126] But the public health journals grew increasingly uneasy with the concept, accusing its proponents of being synthesizers rather than original thinkers[127] and insisting that preventive and curative medicine could not be linked in the manner they suggested without losing sight of prevention entirely.[128] By 1947, social medicine was being decisively rejected as too clinical and too interested in social pathology as opposed to health. An editorial in the *Lancet* fuelled the indignation of the *Medical Officer* by deeming it appropriate that social medicine should have grown out of hospital medicine rather than public health, and acknowledging only that the new social medicine experts would probably require 'some of the public health techniques, such as field studies and the applications of statistics'.[129] The *Medical Officer* was especially scathing in its review of the report of the Oxford Institute on its work between 1943 and 1950, accusing it of ignoring the contribution of public health and describing its account of the introduction of social medicine as 'naive'. The journal was particularly incensed by the Institute's attack on the value of mass radiography and infant welfare clinics.[130]

Thus social medicine became alienated from the practice of public health, but at the same time it failed to have the kind of impact on the medical schools that Ryle had hoped for. Two reports on medical education by the Royal College of Physicians, published in 1943,[131] and by an Inter-Departmental Committee on the Medical Schools, published in 1944,[132] recommended the development of departments of social medicine. However, their definitions of the subject were vague and this in and of itself was part of the problem. The Inter-Departmental Committee talked enthusiastically of a radical reorientation of the medical curriculum and of the need for social medicine to permeate all medical school teaching. Commenting that there was no accepted definition of social medicine, the report gave no clear idea as to how the subject was to be developed and confined itself to stressing the importance of health promotion and of training clinicians in 'social diagnosis'.[133] Both reports focused their attention on the contribution of social medicine to the training of clinicians, and the Inter-Departmental Report, in particular, was infused with the need to raise the social conscience of the medical profession in a manner similar to Ryle's early writings.

Most medical schools, however, reacted to social medicine by slightly modifying their departments of public health, but without fundamentally changing their approach to medical education. Where new chairs of social medicine were established, the new departments had little effect on the rest of the medical schools. Indeed, Ryle's chair was not filled when he died in 1950. Furthermore, a dangerous schism developed between social medicine academics and public health practitioners. This was one of the major problems attracting the attention of the Todd Commission on Medical Education which reported in 1968 and recommended that a new specialty of community medicine be established in order to bridge the gap between the university teachers and practitioners.[134]

Public health and the NHS
By the mid-1940s public health doctors were fighting on two fronts. Not only were academics telling them that public health had little to offer conceptually, but also, after 1944, the plans for an NHS looked increasingly as though they would result in

a reduction in the activities of public health departments.

The ideas contained in the Medical Planning Report issued by the Society of Medical Officers of Health in 1942 were not dissimilar to those of the BMA's Medical Planning Commission.[135] Indeed, the two bodies were closer than they had been for two decades. Even so, MOsH favoured a centralized health health service under the control of the Ministry of Health, while the BMA preferred to see an independent corporation and medical representation on new regional councils, rather than administration by local authorities. The sharpest divergence was over the question of remuneration, MOsH once more recommending whole-time salaried service, to which the BMA was implacably opposed. The Society of Medical Officers of Health showed its weakness by failing to mount an effective campaign to capitalize on the strong position of the public health departments in respect to health service delivery during the 1930s and early 1940s.

The White Paper on the NHS, published in 1944, favoured administrative control by the local authorities but left the position of the MOH in considerable doubt.[136] It proposed to establish a central medical board to administer the GP service; joint boards of county and county borough councils to oversee planning and administration of hospital and consultant services (including TB, VD, mental health and infectious diseases) in their areas; and a local health service administered by the county and county boroughs to look after infant welfare, school health and environmental hygiene. Public health doctors were disappointed that the White Paper did not propose to legislate a truly integrated health system and regretted the lack of reference to preventive medicine.[137] Only nine lines of the White Paper were devoted to the public health service. From Appendix E it was possible to deduce that the proposed joint boards were to be administered by a chief administrative medical officer, to whom the MOH of the county or county borough would be responsible.[138] The precise nature of the MOH's powers was not made clear. The reaction of MOsH was pessimistic. In face of the threat to the MOH's domain, the *Medical Officer* condemned the emphasis the White Paper put on curing disease rather than promoting health (a point also made by some commentators in other

medical journals),[139] and raised the cry that prevention and cure
were separate approaches in order to justify the public health
department retaining its full range of powers and activities.[140]
But, in fact, public health had failed to develop any firm
philosophical basis for this argument, which also flew in the
face of the reality of public health practice during the inter-war
years.

The story of the way in which the White Paper's proposals
were modified in response to the lobbying by the voluntary
hospitals and the BMA has been told elsewhere.[141] Bevan's
final scheme advocated the nationalization of the hospitals,
albeit in such a manner that it may be argued that the methods
of organization used by the voluntary hospitals were largely
preserved.[142] GPs retained their status as independent
contractors, and the local authorities were left with a
substantially reduced mandate for maternal and child welfare,
domiciliary midwifery, health visiting, home nursing, home
helps, vaccination and immunization, ambulance services,
health centres, and prevention and aftercare services. These
changes resulted in the district MOsH in particular losing a
major part of their duties and authority; responsibility for
maternal and child welfare, ambulances, midwives and
vaccination and immunization were all transferred to the
county and county borough levels. The Ministry suggested that
the counties delegate the day-to-day administration (but not the
responsibility) for these services to assistant county MOsH,
who would serve an area comprising one or more districts and
be accountable to the MOH.[143] During 1947 and 1948 the BMA
was busy arranging compensation for district MOsH whose
reduced workload had resulted in their being offered other
'unsuitable jobs'.[144] Efforts to achieve both more uniformity in
the size of local authorities and to rationalize their structure, as
well as experiments in the delegation of powers between levels
of local government, continued during the 1950s and 1960s.
Inevitably the standing of the MOH and the public health
service was affected by what W. Robson called the 'crisis in
local government'.[145]

The mood of MOsH after the Act was passed was extremely
gloomy, and the public health journals harped repeatedly on
the loss of the hospitals and clinics and bewailed 'the remnants

that remain'. The president of the Society of Medical Officers of Health, J. Johnstone Jervis, felt that the only hope lay in the development of health centres, but, of course, this did not occur until the late 1960s.[146] However, E.K. MacDonald, MOH for Leicester, was perceptive in noticing the possibility for instigating new activities under the vaguely worded s.28 of the Act. Section 28 referred to the possibility of providing welfare services for preventing illness, helping those suffering from illness, or for providing aftercare services.[147] Welfare services of this kind did develop rapidly after 1948. The *Medical Officer* also tried to strike a positive note when it remarked that the MOH would at last be free of his hospital administration duties, which the journal had viewed with suspicion from the outset in 1929, and would be able to devote himself to 'epidemiology'.[148] The journal added that the responsibilities for hospital administration had in all probability diverted MOsH from the business of prevention, which accounted for 'the "discovery" of social medicine which had for a century been daily work of the MOH'.[149] H. Paul, the MOH for Smethwick, acknowledged the loss of the hospitals as a blessing in disguise, but commented rightly on the new regional hospital boards' lack of epidemiological expertise and their lack of experience in managing the isolation hospitals and the preventive side of TB control.[150]

In their Annual Reports for 1948 MOsH were often frank in bemoaning their fate. Most voiced regret at the loss of the hospital service. The MOH for Bournemouth told his readers that:

Having regard to the new order of things it may surprise some to know that your MOH, who for 21 years has been medical superintendent of all the institutions controlled by the Public Health Committee and acted as Group Hospital Officer for Bournemouth, Poole and Christchurch during the War, has not opportunity of expressing his views to a Hospital or Sanatorium Management Committee or even of hearing the opinions expressed by others.[151]

The MOH for the North Riding of Yorkshire complained that hospital and sanatorium staffs stopped supplying information on patients admitted and discharged which made if difficult for the public health department to discharge its responsibility for

aftercare.[152] In Nottinghamshire, the MOH commented dryly
that liaison was an 'overworked and often meaningless
word'.[153] The MOH for Salford also regretted the absence of
effective integration of the health service and that the NHS in
fact appeared to be a 'sickness' service: 'A tragedy of our times
is that so much is being spent on negative health; so
comparatively little on positive health. Oh the pity of it—the
pity of it!'[154]

Most commentators agreed that the public health department was but 'a shell' of its former self, and early in 1950 the
editor of the *Medical Officer* was still afraid that 'MOsH may
be elbowed out of existence altogether'.[155] R.H. Parry,
professor of public health at Bristol, warned MOsH that they
were 'on a sinking ship'. With the MOH bearing responsibility
for a considerable burden of welfare work but for little in the
way of clinical duties, he could see no reason for local health
authorities to require the services of a fully-qualified medical
advisor in the long term.[156] Few felt able to agree with the
optimistic view of F. Grundy, professor of preventive medicine
in the University of Wales (and author of a textbook whose title
changed in response to the shifts in academic thinking from *A
Handbook of Social Medicine* (1945), to *The New Public Health*
(1949), to *Preventive Medicine and Public Health* (1951)), that
MOsH should begin to develop information services, carry out
epidemiological research, and serve as the effective link
between the three parts of the NHS.[157]

Medical officers of health were also disappointed that they
failed to secure any compensatory gains in terms of pay and
status as a result of the 1946 Act. Hopes that the MOH might
have achieved specialist status were dashed. The salary of some
fifty MOsH serving the largest populations was equivalent to
that of specialists, and the *Medical Officer* counselled that
specialist status *per se* was 'not worth a fuss'.[158] But as one
disgruntled MOH pointed out, the MOH 'has been accorded
no status except by word of mouth, whether professional or
financial'.[159] The practice was still for local authorities to relate
the salary of MOsH to that of local government employees
rather than to that of other doctors, and the salary of MOsH
was decided by negotiations with the Whitley Council
machinery rather than with the BMA.

It was little wonder that MOsH at the time and since looked back on public health during the inter-war years as some kind of golden age in comparison with their position after the NHS came into being. In terms of initiatives that the public health departments took in developing new services during the inter-war period, there is some justification for this perception. For example, the MOH for Reading and the *Medical Officer* justly drew attention to the rapid decline in preventive dentistry after 1948,[160] although the scale of provision of this service by local authorities was very limited during the 1930s. The TB service, which was extensive, was also effectively dismantled and there is no doubt but that this would have caused severe problems had the incidence of TB not declined. The aims of MOsH for a national health service were also more radical than what actually transpired. The Society of Medical Officers of Health had called for an integrated, centralized and salaried service. However, public health departments during the 1920s and 1930s must be criticized for their failure both to address crucial health issues (particularly in relation to unemployment and nutrition) and to develop a firm rationale for their work. It seems that public health doctors were happy to extend their activities in whatever direction the Ministry permitted and anticipated that eventually this gap-filling exercise would be transformed into a fully-fledged state medical service in which they would play a dominant role. It was a dream doomed to disappointment, for neither the Ministry nor the medical profession shared it. Thus in 1948 the public health service was left to lick its wounds. The immediate inclination of public health doctors was not to follow Grundy's injunction to reorient their work towards the gathering of local health statistics and information and the promotion of effective integration,[161] but rather to look for new services to administer.

NOTES

1. C. Webster 'Britain's Experience of Socialized Medicine', lecture series given at the Wellcome Unit, Oxford.
2. S. Chave, 'The Medical Officer of Health, 1847–1974', *Proc. Roy. Soc. Med.*, 67 (1974), pp. 1243–7.

3. J. Johnstone Jervis, 'Has public health any future?', *Public Health*, 59 (1946), p. 46.
4. 'First reactions to the White Paper', *Public Health*, 57 (1944), pp. 74–8.
5. P.P. 'Report of the Committee on Local Authority and Allied Personal Social Services', Cmnd. 3703, 1967–8, xxxii.
6. C. Webster, 'Health, welfare and unemployment during the Depression', *Past and Present* (forthcoming).
7. J.E. Pater, *The Making of the NHS* (London: King Edward's Hospital Fund for London, 1981), pp. 106–8.
8. P.P. 'Report of the Consultative Council on Medical and Allied Services', Cmd. 693, 1920, xvii, p. 1001.
9. *ibid.*, para. 3.
10. *ibid.,* para. 6.
11. *ibid.*, para. 24.
12. Lord Dawson, 'Medicine and the state', *Medical Officer*, 23 (1920), pp. 223–4.
13. C. Webster 'Britain's Experience of Socialized Medicine'; F. Honigsbaum, *The Division in British Medicine* (London: Kogan Page, 1979); J. Morgan and K.O. Morgan, *Portrait of a Progressive: The Political Career of Christopher, Viscount Addison* (Oxford: Clarendon Press, 1980).
14. G. Newman, 'The Place of Public Opinion in Preventive Medicine' (London: Ministry of Health, 1920), lecture to the National Health Society.
15. G. Newman, 'The state and the future of medical practice', *Medical Officer*, 24 (1920), pp. 5–7.
16. G. Newman, 'The Foundation of National Health' (London: Ministry of Health, 1928), the Charles Hastings Lecture.
17. Ministry of Health, *An Outline of the Practice of Preventive Medicine*, memorandum by Sir George Newman (London: HMSO, 1926), paras 43–50.
18. G. Newman, *Recent Advances in Medical Education in England* (London: HMSO, 1923), p. 156.
19. 'Health services', editorial, *Public Health*, 34 (1921), p. 159.
20. J. Lewis, *The Politics of Motherhood* (London: Croom Helm, 1980), pp. 29–30, 95, 104.
21. 'The place of preventive medicine in the medical curriculum', editorial, *Public Health*, 33 (1920), p. 175.
22. BMA Archives, Medico-Sociological Committee, item 2001, documents 1920–1.
23. *ibid.*, 13/5/21 meeting, views of Dr J. Robertson.
24. *ibid.*, 8/4/21 meeting, views of Dr T. Shaddick Higgins.
25. GMC, *Public Health Resolutions and Rules for Diplomas or Degrees in Sanitary Science, Public Health or State Medicine* (London: GMC, 1930),
26. BMA Archives, Medico-Sociological Committee, item 2001, 3/6/21, 'Draft Conclusions and Recommendations by the Chairman, Dr E. Rowland Fothergill'.

27. Association of County Medical Officers of Health Archives, Wellcome Institute, (hereafter CMO), A3, meeting of the Association, 22/3/29.
28. For evidence of the BMA's attitude to salaried doctors see its response to the LGB's scheme for maternal and child welfare issued in 1914: 'Special Report of the Council on maternal and child welfare schemes', *BMJ*, I (1915), Supplement, pp. 230–3, and *BMJ*, I (1917), p. 430.
29. 'The public health service', editorial, *Medical Officer*, 34 (1925), p. 99.
30. C. Webster, 'Healthy or hungry Thirties?', *History Workshop Journal*, 13 (1982), pp. 110–29; and Lewis, *Politics of Motherhood*.
31. 'BMA's Private Practice Committee's Interim Report on Encroachments on the Sphere of Private Practice by the Activities of Local Authorities', *BMJ*, II (1928), Supplement, pp. 185–96.
32. 'Report by Medical Secretary on Investigation into the Operation of Maternal and Child Welfare Centres and School Clinics in Certain Areas', *BMJ*, II (1928), Supplement, p. 194.
33. *ibid.*, p. 190.
34. 'BMA's Private Practice Committee's Interim Report on Encroachments', p. 187.
35. 'Report on Encroachments on the Sphere of Private Practice', *BMJ*, I (1929), p. 130.
36. *ibid.*, p. 132.
37. 'Preventive medicine and health insurance', editorial, *Medical Officer*, 44 (1930), p. 199.
38. 'Encroachments on private practice', editorial, *Medical Officer*, 41, (1929), p. 31.
39. 'Health authorities and private medical practice', editorial, *Medical Officer*, 40 (1928), p. 217.
40. Honigsbaum, *Division in British Medicine*, p. 138.
41. G. Buchan, 'British public health and its present trend', *Public Health*, 45 (1931), p. 9.
42. 'Scale of minimum commencing salaries for public health medical officers', *BMJ*, I, Suppplement (1923), pp. 151–8, and 'Cooperation with the Society of Medical Officers of Health', *BMJ*, II, Supplement (1923), pp. 35–41.
43. 'The Society of Medical Officers of Health and the BMA', *Medical Officer*, 30 (1923), p. 87.
44. Letter from W.G. Booth, MOH for Lincolnshire, printed in the editorial column, *Public Health*, 52 (1939), p. 89.
45. Society of Medical Officers of Health Archives, Wellcome Unit, Oxford (hereafter SMOH), A12, Minutes of the Council of the Society, 17/2/39.
46. BMA Archives, Public Health Committee, 1929, item 1859, meeting of representatives of the CCA, Assn. Mun. Corps, UDCs Assn, RDCs Assn, Assn Ed. Cttees, Mental Hosps Assn, BMA and Soc. MOsH, 14/2/29.
47. *ibid.*
48. E.H.T. Nash, 'The public health service in the future', *Public Health*, 48 (1934), p. 9.

49. 'The public health service', editorial, *Medical Officer*, 58 (1937), p. 95, and 'The Royal Sanitary Institute Congress at Scarborough', *Medical Officer*, 62 (1939), p. 27.
50. SMOH, E19, W.W. Jameson and R.M.F. Picken, 'The Appointment of Medical Officers of Health', February 1936.
51. C.O. Stallybrass, 'Some aspects of hospital administration', *Public Health*, 46 (1933), pp. 159-62.
52. A. Massey, 'The doctor as administrator', *Public Health*, 50 (1937), pp. 117-20.
53. 'Medicine and the state', editorial, *Medical Officer*, 44 (1930), p. 245; and 'The present state of preventive medicine', editorial, *Medical Officer*, 50 (1933), p. 21.
54. *ibid.*
55. 'Medicine and the state', *Medical Officer*, 44 (1930), p. 21.
56. 'Preventive medicine in 1930', editorial, *Medical Officer*, 45 (1931), p. 1.
57. 'The public health service', editorial, *Medical Officer*, 58 (1937), p. 95.
58. J. Ferguson, 'Hospital policy in relation to preventive medicine', *Public Health*, 51 (1938), p. 239.
59. W.G. Savage, 'Our future', *Public Health*, 49 (1935), p. 42.
60. J. Grant, 'An investigation of diphtheria carriers', *BMJ*, II (1931), p. 566.
61. L. Bryder, 'The problems of tuberculosis in England and Wales, 1900-1950', unpub. D. Phil. thesis, Oxford University, 1985.
62. C. Killick Millard, 'Inoculation against diphtheria', *Medical Officer*, 53 (1935), pp. 85-7.
63. R.M.F. Picken, 'The changing relations between the medical officer of health and the medical profession', *Public Health*, 52 (1939), p. 262.
64. R. Cattell, *The Fight for our National Intelligence* (London: P.S. King, 1937).
65. Webster, 'Healthy or hungry thirties?', p. 114.
66. *ibid.*
67. Lewis, *Politics of Motherhood,* p. 104.
68. 'Malnutrition', editorial, *Medical Officer*, 52 (1934), p. 57.
69. Webster, 'Health, welfare and unemployment'.
70. M. Spring Rice, *Working Class Wives* (London: Virago, 1981; first pub., 1939).
71. Women's Group on Public Welfare, *Our Towns* (Oxford: Oxford University Press, 1943). See also the debate over the accuracy of Titmuss's conclusions between Lewis, *Politics of Motherhood*, p. 179, and Webster, 'Healthy or hungry Thirties?', p. 116, on the one side and J.M. Winter, 'Infant mortality, maternal mortality and public health in Britain in the 1930s', *Journal of European Economic History*, 8 (1979), p. 451, on the other side.
72. R. Titmuss, *Birth, Poverty and Wealth* (London: Hamish Hamilton, 1943).
73. J. Young, 'An address on maternal morbidity from puerperal sepsis', *BMJ*, II (1928), p. 967; and 'The woman damaged from childbearing', *BMJ*, I (1929), pp. 891-5.

74. J. Young, 'The medical schools and the nation's health', *Lancet*, I (1933), pp. 119-20.
75. G.C.M. McGonigle, 'The biological concept of preventive medicine', *Public Health*, 43 (1930), p. 239.
76. J. Lewis and B. Brookes, 'A reassessment of the work of the Peckham Health Centre, 1926-51', *Milbank Memorial Quarterly, Health and Society*, 61 (1983), p. 311.
77. McGonigle, 'The biological concept of preventive medicine', p. 239.
78. G.C.M. McGonigle and J. Kirby, *Poverty and Public Health* (London: Gollancz, 1936), pp. 108-27.
79. Lewis, *Politics of Motherhood*, p. 175.
80. *ibid.*
81. *ibid.*, p. 184.
82. *ibid.*, p. 49.
83. 'The public medical service', editorial, *Medical Officer*, 52 (1934), p. 81.
84. C. Thompson, 'The medical profession and the future', *Medical officer*, 53 (1935), pp. 165-8.
85. BMA, *A General Medical Service for the Nation* (London: BMA, 1938), para. 5.
86. C. Hill and Maitland Radford, 'The future of general medical practice', *Public Health*, 50 (1937), pp. 145-7.
87. C. Webster, 'Britain's Experience of Socialized Medicine', lecture series given at the Wellcome Unit, Oxford.
88. J.A. Ryle, 'Social medicine: its meaning and scope', *BMJ*, II (1943), pp. 633-6.
89. J.A. Ryle, 'Today and tomorrow', *BMJ*, II (1940), p. 657.
90. R.M. Titmuss, *Problems of Social Policy* (London: HMSO, 1950).
91. Quoted by R. Means and R. Smith, *The Development of Welfare Services for Elderly People* (London: Croom Helm, 1985), p. 123.
92. Titmuss Papers, untitled paper on social medicine TS, 21/12/42. I am grateful to Mrs Kay Titmuss for allowing me to see the as yet uncatalogued papers she has in her possession. Hereafter these papers are referred to as 'Titmuss Papers (private)'.
93. Medical Planning Commission, 'Draft Interim Report', *BMJ*, I (1942), pp. 743-53.
94. Honigsbaum, *Division in British Medicine,* p. 186.
95. Medical Planning Research, 'Interim General Report', *Lancet*, II (1942), Supplement, pp. 599-622.
96. S. Wilson Jameson, 'War and the advancement of social medicine', *Lancet*, II (1942), p. 475.
97. 'Social medicine', editorial, *Lancet*, I (1943), p. 51.
98. 'The place of social medicine in the reorganization of the health services', *BMJ*, I (1942), pp. 703-4.
99. J.A. Ryle, letter, *BMJ*, II (1942), p. 801.
100. J.A. Ryle, 'The Obligations of Medicine', 20/12/42, Ryle Papers, 20/9, Wellcome Unit, Oxford.
101. Letters from J.A. Ryle, R. McCarrison and C. McNeil, *BMJ*, I (1942), pp. 51 and 109.

102. Ryle, 'Social medicine', p. 633.
103. F.A.E. Crewe, 'Social medicine as an academic discipline and an instrument of social policy', *Lancet*, II (1944), pp. 617–19.
104. F.A.E. Crewe, 'Social medicine as an academic discipline', in *Modern Trends in Public Health*, ed A. Massey (London: Butterworths, 1949), p. 73.
105. Major A. Greenwood, 'Social medicine', *BMJ*, I (1946), p. 117. G. Rosen, *From Medical Police to Social Medicine: Essays in the History of Health Care* (New York: Science History Publications, 1974), p. 111.
106. J.A. Ryle, *Changing Disciplines* (Oxford: Oxford University Press, 1949), p. 7.
107. Crewe, 'Social medicine as an academic discipline'; and L. Hogben, 'Social medicine in the universities', *Medical Officer*, 71 (1944), pp. 37–9.
108. D. Armstrong, *The Political Anatomy of the Body* (Cambridge: Cambridge University Press, 1983), p. 46. On the development of survey methodology see also M. Bulmer ed., *Essays in the History of British Sociological Research* (Cambridge: Cambridge University Press, 1985).
109. *First Annual Report of the Social Medicine Research Unit* (MRC, 1949).
110. J.N. Morris and R.M. Titmuss, 'Health and social change I: the recent history of rheumatic heart disease', *Medical Officer*, 72 (1944), pp. 69–71.
111. J.A. Ryle to R.M. Titmuss, 13/10/43, Titmuss Papers (private).
112. J.A. Ryle to C.O. Stallybrass, 10/7/44, Ryle Papers, 20/82, Wellcome Unit Oxford.
113. MRC Archives, 418, Vol. I, Social Medicine Research Unit, Edward Mellanby to J.N. Morris, 2/2/48.
114. *ibid.*, J.N. Morris to E. Mellanby, 9/1/48.
115. Ryle, *Changing Disciplines*.
116. E. Richard Weinerman, *Social Medicine in Western Europe* (School of Public Health, University of California, 1951), pp. 12–13.
117. S. Leff, *Social Medicine* (London: Routledge & Kegan Paul, 1953), pp. 12–13.
118. Ryle, *Changing Disciplines*, pp. 11–12.
119. W. Hobson, 'What is social medicine?', *BMJ*, II (1949), p. 125.
120. *ibid.*
121. W. Hobson, 'Social Medicine as a University Discipline', December 1947, Inaugural Lecture, University of Sheffield.
122. 'Social medicine', editorial, *Medical Officer*, 68 (1942), p. 19.
123. 'The institution of social medicine', editorial, *ibid.*, pp. 50–1.
124. W.G. Booth, 'Social medicine', *Public Health*, 56 (1943), pp. 80–2.
125. J.D. Kershaw, 'The task of social medicine', *Medical Officer*, 70 (1943), pp. 197–9.
126. SMOH, Cl/I, Minutes of the County Borough Group, July 1945.
126. 'Social medicine', editorial, *Medical Officer*, 71 (1944), p. 33.
128. 'Preventive and curative medicine', editorial, *Medical Officer*, 71 (1944), p. 177.
129. 'Social pathology', editorial, *Lancet*, I (1947), p. 413; 'Social

pathology', editorial, *Medical Officer*, 77 (1947), p. 161.
130. 'The Oxford Institute of Social Medicine', editorial, *Medical Officer*, 85 (1951), p. 12.
131. Royal College of Physicians of London, Social and Preventive Medicine Committee, *Interim Report* (London: Royal College of Physicians, 1943), p. 3.
132. Ministry of Health and Department of Health for Scotland, *Report of the Inter-Departmental Committee on Medical Schools* (London: HMSO, 1944).
133. *ibid.*, p. 167.
134. P.P., 'Report of the Royal Commission on Medical Education', Cmnd. 3569, 1967–8, xxv, p. 569, para. 133. See below, p. 104.
135. 'Medical Planning—the Society's Report', editorial, *Public Health*, 55 (1942), p. 197.
136. Ministry of Health and Department of Health for Scotland, *A National Health Service*, Cmd. 6502 (London: HMSO, 1944).
137. 'White Paper', editorial, *Public Health*, 57 (1944), p. 61; and 'A National Health Service', editorial, *Medical Officer*, 71 (1944), p. 66.
138. Cmd. 6502, App. E, 'Finance of the new services', pp. 80–5.
139. 'White Paper reviewed: VI: By an urban practitioner', *Lancet*, I (1944), p. 443.
140. 'Social problems and health', editorial, *Medical Officer*, 71 (1944), p. 161; and 'Preventive and Curative Medicine', editorial, *ibid.*, p. 177.
141. Pater, *The Making of the NHS;* and R. Klein, *The Politics of the NHS* (London: Longmans, 1983); Honigsbaum, *The Division in British Medicine*.
142. C. Webster, 'Britain's Experience of Socialized Medicine', lecture series given at the Wellcome Unit, Oxford.
143. W.A. Robson, *Local Government in Crisis* (London: Allen & Unwin, 1966), p. 33; E.W. Cohen, *Autonomy and Delegation in Local Government* (London: Institute of Public Administration, n.d.), p. 53.
144. BMA Archives, Public Health Committee, 1947–8, Item 1506, Doc. 23, 'The Position under Proposed County Scheme of Delegation of MOsH of County Districts which are Welfare Authorities'; Doc. 24, 'Health Services to be Provided by LHAs under Pt. III of the Act'; Doc. 25, 'Sub. Cttee. Meeting of County District MOsH, 27/2/48'.
145. Robson, *Local Government in Crisis*.
146. J. Johnstone Jervis, 'Has public health any future?', *Public Health*, 59 (1946), pp. 46–9.
147. E.K. MacDonald, 'The challenge of Section 28', *Public Health*, 61 (1947), pp. 37–8.
148. 'Clinical and preventive medicine', editorial, *Medical Officer*, 78 (1948), p. 175.
149. 'The MOH and the hospital board', editorial, *Medical Officer*, 79 (1948), pp. 258–9.
150. H. Paul, 'The making of the National Health Service Act, 1946', *Medical Officer*, 85 (1951), pp. 201–7.
151. *Annual Report of the MOH for Bournemouth CB, 1948*, p. 4.

152. *Annual Report of the MOH for North Riding of Yorkshire, 1948*, pp. 4–5.
153. *Annual Report of the MOH for Nottinghamshire, 1948*, p. 15.
154. *Annual Report of the MOH for Salford CB, 1948*, p. 7.
155. 'The future of the MOH', editorial, *Medical Officer*, 83 (1950), p. 2.
156. SMOH, Cl/I, Minutes of County Borough Group, paper by Professor R.H. Parry, Annual Meeting, 1947.
157. F. Grundy, 'New paths for public health', *Public Health*, 63 (1953), pp. 190–2.
158. 'The public health service and the profession', editorial, *Medical Officer*, 81 (1949), p. 31.
159. A MOH, 'Conditions of service and of recruitment to the public health service', *ibid.*, p. 24.
160. *Annual Report of the MOH of Reading CB, 1948*, p. 5; 'Retrospect in Nottinghamshire', editorial, *Medical Officer*, 85 (1951), p. 145.
161. Grundy, 'New paths for public health'.

2 Pressure from within and without: public health 1950–1968

In the tripartite health service that persisted (albeit in different administrative form) after 1948, the work of public health departments was confined to what were often referred to as community health services, where community was defined as excluding the hospital. (The attempt to redefine community to include the hospital since 1974 has never entirely succeeded.) MOsH were engaged mainly in the delivery of community health services, in which social work grew rapidly in importance, and struggled to bring order out of the bewildering complexity of local authority jurisdictions and structures. During the 1950s, MOsH bitterly resisted the attempts of their local authority employers to label them 'administrators with medical knowledge', which was in large part responsible for the low pay of public health doctors and their low status in the eyes of other doctors. While they resisted attempts at lay control from within the local authority structure, the character and the future of public health departments were nevertheless closely bound up with local government. Public health work found itself trapped within the complicated and hierarchical local authority structure and in large part dependent on the achievement of local government reform.

In the post-war period, public health was forced to cast around for a new niche. In all its relationships—with local authorities, with the NHS and with other doctors—its place was by no means clearly defined. There was no satisfactory philosophical underpinning for the variety of duties and services public health departments were made responsible for under the NHS Act. From the late 1950s government policy was committed to increasing the provision of 'community

care' for both the elderly and the mentally ill. Indeed the
Hospital Plan of 1962 was born partly out of the pressure to
reduce the in-patient population in mental hospitals. Responsibility for community care fell largely on the public health
departments. But, as A. Walker has pointed out, community
care meant different things at different times and in relation to
different groups in need.[1] In respect to the elderly, where it was
originally intended to mean domiciliary care, it was reinter-
preted to include local authority residential care. Thus both the
Hospital Plan of 1962 and the local authorities' Health and
Welfare Plans of 1963 envisaged the expansion of residential
provision. In the meantime, the shortage of beds in both
sectors resulted in increasing confusion as to the boundaries
between the two types of care.[2]

In the absence of both principle and planning in respect to
community care, and with the failure either firmly to
distinguish community care from institutional provision or to
increase the flow of resources to domiciliary care, the Ministry
of Health resorted to exhorting the different parts of the health
services to co-operate and co-ordinate their activities as a
means to achieving community care.[3] Medical officers of
health were seen as the principal co-ordinators of community
health services, but they found that their efforts were not always
appreciated, especially by GPs with whom they shared the
health territory outside the hospital. While the introduction of
the NHS eliminated the conflict between private and state
medicine which had underpinned the 1930s encroachment
debate, GPs and public health doctors continued to vie with
one another in their claim to do personal preventive work.

By the end of the 1950s, academic leaders in the field, many
of whom had been active proponents of social medicine in the
1940s, were pressing for a redefinition of medical administration as a means to providing MOsH with a basis for
specialization and thereby a better standing in the medical
profession. Courses in public health were revised and
'administration' defined to mean strategies for the health
services as a whole, rather than the day-to-day administration
of the services for which the MOH had statutory responsibility.
However, the gulf between academics and practitioners was
such that it is doubtful how far this attempt to find a new role

for senior public health doctors (little mention was made of the clinic doctors) was understood by the MOsH. Certainly, confusion over the meaning of administration persisted long after reorganization of the NHS in 1974, when administration, broadly defined, became a major component of the work of many of the new community physicians.

In the end, change in the position of the MOH and the public health department was forced in the late 1960s by the pressure of the social work lobby, spearheaded in large part by academic social scientists such as R. Titmuss. Titmuss saw the establishment of unified personal social service departments as a means first to achieving professional autonomy for social workers; second to providing better back-up for the hard-pressed family doctor (whose discontent had culminated in the 1965 movement for mass resignations from the NHS); and third to developing community care more effectively. M. Brown, for example, believed strongly that the concept of community care owed more to the development of social work, including group work and community work as well as individual casework, than it did to public health.[4] Just as the public health doctor was not able successfully to justify his continued work in personal prevention, so he also failed to make a good case for the medical administration of welfare work. Thus MOsH increasingly found themselves accused of failure in respect to the delivery of effective community care, and squeezed between the twin pressures of general practice from without and social work from within.

'THIRD GRADE DOCTORS'?

In striking his rare note of optimism after the passing of the NHS Act, F. Grundy, professor of public health, welcomed the opportunity offered by the Act for the MOH both to engage more actively in epidemiological research and to shed his more onerous day-to-day administrative duties.[5] It is not clear that MOsH succeeded in doing either. During the early 1950s, the public health journals stressed the importance of studying the epidemiology of chronic disease. The editor of the *Medical Officer* put it bluntly: 'Let us face the facts. The study of the control of notifiable infectious diseases is no longer the main task of the medical officer of health. But, the journal continued, 'does he realize it? It would appear not.'[6] Certainly at the Royal Society of Health Congress of 1953 Dr J.F. Warin, MOH for Oxford, opened a session on 'The Tasks Ahead' by stressing the importance of infectious disease control and the problems of many other long-established services. In the course of the discussion, the MOH for Nottingham expressed concern that public health seemed to be obsessed with 'the old question of how to get along with services which we have already got' and lodged a plan for more attention to subjects such as nutrition education and studies of fatigue.[7] However, as the president of the Society of Medical Officers of Health observed, the annual reports of MOsH yielded little evidence of new endeavours of this kind.[8] The MOH for Coventry questioned Grundy's assumptions that administrative tasks had diminished since 1948.[9] For while MOsH were no longer responsible for hospital administration they rapidly became immersed in the administration of ambulance services and of services under Part III of the Act; the MOH for Caernarvonshire named home helps and old people's homes as the most time-consuming.[10] Responsibility for both services also served to embed the MOH and the public health department more firmly in the culture and concerns of unreformed local government.

In 1951 MOsH were incensed by the view expressed by the local authorities associations that MOsH were but 'administrators with medical knowledge', implying that they had no connection with the mainstream of medicine and were fulfilling a largely executive function. The *Medical Officer* commented that while public health doctors had survived the old abuse that they were 'drains doctors' or, worse, 'sewer rats', this form of attack was more insidious.[11] This perception was correct in so far as public health doctors spent the whole period fighting the insistence of local authorities that they should be paid on a scale comparable to other administrative officers rather than to other doctors. In 1950 pay negotiations through the Whitley Council machinery broke down and the case went to industrial arbitration, the first time a profession was heard in industrial court.[12]

Public health doctors were disappointed with the decision of the court. Population was retained as the criterion determining the salaries of MOsH and the proposal of the management side to the effect that a range of minimum salaries should be laid down for each population group was adopted. This meant that each local authority was allowed some discretion in fixing the commencing salary, having regard not only to population but also 'other local factors [such as the salaries of other chief officers] and the functional responsibilities of their medical officer of health post'.[13] By the early 1960s, salary increases for MOsH had become tied to those for other chief officers in local government.[14] MOsH serving the largest populations (400–600,000) earned a maximum of £3,390 in 1958, £365 short of a consultant in receipt of the lowest distinction award. However, the position of assistant MOs was much worse. Local authorities insisted on fixing their salaries on the same scale as lay administrators and their maximum pay (£1,475 in 1958) fell well below the £2,350 maximum for an MO in the most junior grade of the civil service. Furthermore, assistant MOs outnumbered all the other grades of medical officer together. In 1967 M. Warren and J. Cooper calculated that only 8 per cent of public health doctors were full MOsH. Sixty per cent of full-time MOs were in the lowest grade of assistant MO, and the remaining 40 per cent were almost equally divided between the five grades of senior assistant MO, senior or principal MO, divisional MO, deputy MOH and MOH. As Warren and Cooper pointed out, only a fraction could hope to rise to a top post in the field.[15]

The government refused to include MOsH in the remit of the 1962 Royal Commission on Doctors' and Dentists' Pay. Sir Allen Daley, former principal school medical officer for the LCC, concluded that the government had no wish to antagonize the local authorities or put itself in a position where it might be compelled to pay public health doctors out of Exchequer funds.[16] Throughout the early 1960s, the staff side of the Whitley Council was instructed by the conference of public health doctors to pursue parity with other doctors.

Thus public health doctors were deemed to be doing primarily administrative, routine work and were paid accordingly. By the early 1960s academics in the field were making a strong case for 'medical administration' as specialized work, not in the sense of institutional administration as was the case in the 1930s, but rather in the hope that MOsH would become broadly based 'health strategists'.[17] However to practitioners, administration continued to mean the day-to-day administration and co-ordination of public health services. In Warren and Cooper's 1966 survey of 546 MOsH (90 per cent of the total number) and their staffs, the work of the MOsH, their deputies and of divisional MOs were reported as being mainly administrative and concerned with environmental and/or personal health services.[18] Over half the principal or senior MOs also had administrative duties, usually in conjunction with their responsibility for maternal and child welfare. The rest, together with the assistant MOs, were engaged primarily in clinical work.

The MOH for Gloucestershire was one of the very few to state publicly that he was proud to work for local government.[19] Not only were public health doctors low paid relative to their medical colleagues (this alone caused the editor of the *Medical Officer* to wonder whether public health should not cease to be controlled by local authorities),[20] but they had also to cope with the complicated structure of local government and of public health administration within it (see Appendix I).

As a result of the NHS Act, district MOsH surrendered responsibility for the personal health services to the county level. In particular, they resented losing responsibility for maternal and child welfare and with their formal charge reduced largely to environmental health, they faced considerable frustration unless either districts were combined to provide a larger unit of administration, or the county was prepared to decentralize.[21] No rule or pattern was established on either of these options. About 70 per cent of MOsH were responsible for areas with populations of less than 100,000, and despite combining districts, 30 per cent served populations of less than 50,000 in 1965.[22] This, of course, reflected what Robson called the 'grotesque' difference in size of local authorities generally.[23] Much of the debate about local government reform and health service administration centred on the optimum size of population to be served. On average, general hospital management committees served 300,000 in the mid-1960s, but the suggestions for the administration of local services tended to favour a population of 100,000. (In 1974, the optimum size for the new districts administering all health services was put at 250,000.)

Many counties decentralized their responsibilities after 1948, appointing a district MOH as an assistant county MO. This was called a 'mixed appointment'. However, not all district MOsH could be appointed as assistant or divisional MOs and not all counties chose to decentralize until forced to do so by the Local Government Act 1958. The nature of appointments held by MOs could be extremely complex and caused considerable confusion, not least in determining pay. For example, in 1952 the BMA was forced to consider the case of Dr J. Sims-Roberts who spent 22 per cent of his time as assistant county MO for Buckinghamshire, 20 per cent as MOH for Aylesbury Borough Council, 23 per cent as MOH for Aylesbury Rural District Council, 10 per cent as MOH for Winslow Rural District Council and 25 per cent as MO to the Regional Hospital Board.[24] To all intents and purposes he thus held a 'combined' post (amalgamating the work of three district councils) within a 'mixed' one, with some RHB work thrown in for good measure. However, the districts concerned had not formally combined; each had appointed him separately, while surrendering the right to terminate the appointment individually. Because pay scales were determined by size of population, the case turned on whether the post was a combined as well as a mixed one. It was not altogether surprising that in its references to public health, the Guillebaud Committee on the costs of the NHS managed to confuse the responsibilities of the county and district MOH.[25] To compound the confusion, school health work, performed under the Education Act 1944 had to be grafted on to public health administration; in two places it remained the case that the MOH did not also fill the position of principal school MO, which complicated the administration of the two services.

Public health doctors experienced considerable tension in reconciling their role in local government with their professional aspirations. In many respects the success of the MOH continued to rest on how well he handled his public health committee. One medical officer fondly remembered the MOH he had worked for until 1948 as someone who had 'bludgeoned his committees to accept all his proposals and if some new and inexperienced councillor queried the wisdom of his advice, he glared at him, bellowed and roared, and soon reduced him (or her) to silence'.[26] Not surprisingly MOsH opinions of local politicians were usually ambivalent. MOsH also found that their professional opinion often ran counter to that of local authority associations, the most damaging example from the public health point of view being the opposition the Society of Medical Officers of Health encountered from the County Councils' Association over the future of social workers employed by local authorities.[27] But MOsH also found both their personal status and claim to professional autonomy threatened by the internal structure and culture of local government. They were anxious to be regarded as doctors first and local government officers second, but they still had to deal with inter-officer and inter-departmental rivalries within the local authority bureaucracy. In many respects, the public health department perforce resembled the hierarchical, authoritarian pattern of departmental organization in local government, which offended groups such as sanitary inspectors and health visitors, as well as challenging the professional autonomy cherished by the medical profession.

In terms of their fellow chief officers, MOsH seem to have experienced greatest rivalry with the town clerk. The movement for greater administrative efficiency in local government emphasized the role of the clerk as the chief administrative officer throughout the 1950s and early 1960s.[28] The *Medical Officer* reported in 1953 that in one Cheshire county borough, the divisional MO's Annual Report had been signed first by the clerk and second by the MO, which smacked of encroachment by the lay administrator on the medical administrator's preserve.[29] Similarly, MOsH resisted attempts in the late 1960s to appoint chief executive officers, arguing that 'the notion that administration exists as a separate entity rather than as a means of putting into practice new services is erroneous'.[30] In fact, the fight to develop and sustain medical administration since World War II has been conducted in the face of opposition both from the medical profession and from the growth of theories which sought to make organizational management a specialized field in and of itself.[31]

Public health doctors also experienced considerable difficulty in defining the parameters of medical administration. A 1966 survey of county MOsH about their views of the relationship between health and welfare in local government, undertaken in response to the appointment of the Seebohm Committee, revealed the often whimsical and *ad hoc* ways in which local government departments and committees were organized and how the MOH and the health department could easily be out-manoeuvred. For example, Dr J. Lyons, who favoured joint health and welfare departments described how it was his opinion that in Devonshire a special sub-committee had been constituted to bring about an amalgamation of the welfare and children's departments against the express wishes of both the children's officer and himself.[32] Like those of many others his account showed how internal organization depended largely on the retirement or death of one of the chief officers and extensive politicking by departments and councillors. In Oxfordshire the ingredients were the same as in Devonshire, but the pattern rather different. Here the amalgamation of health and welfare was recommended twice, in 1958 and 1963, but only came about in 1964 when the county welfare officer retired.[33] In Berkshire the MOH felt strongly that council members played too great a part in determining policy guidelines on such matters.[34]

The MOH and the public health department had to be prepared to stake out territorial claims within the local government structure, but, while they strongly resisted being identified with local government, many MOsH nevertheless became very much a part of the culture of the local authority and ran their departments in the hierarchical fashion that was typical of local government. Sanitary inspectors were the first occupational group within public health departments to claim autonomy from the control of the MOH in the 1950s. The MOH for Reading laid the blame for the difficult relationship between some MOsH and sanitary inspectors firmly on social medicine:

Some of it is undoubtedly due to empire building on the part of a few public health inspectors, but I suggest that there may well be another reason. The sanitarians . . . knew a great deal about such matters as housing, drainage, pure milk supplies and infectious diseases, and were able to gain the respect of sanitary inspectors. Now there seems to be a tendency for them to be replaced by the social medicine addicts who are quite happy to leave things to the public health inspector and then complain if there are symptoms of separationism.[35]

The comment is more interesting for the evidence it provides of the continuing antagonism of many practitioners towards academic social medicine than it is for its analysis of the cause of the problem. Increasingly sanitary inspectors, or public health inspectors as they became in 1956, developed their own specialist training and enjoyed the support of the Ministry of Health in seeking control over their work.

Another group in the public health department, the health visitors, also had cause to be dissatisfied with the control exercised by the MOH, but they never managed to assert their professional independence as did the sanitary inspectors. Later and more disastrously from the MOH's point of view, the social workers also asserted their claim to autonomy. Health visitors were constantly frustrated by the failure properly to define their role, despite the report of a committee of inquiry devoted to the problem in 1956.[36] In all probability, this failure was due in large part to the fact that health visitors did not have the responsibility for designing the service they provided. As one recent commentator has concluded, the control of the MOH contributed to the perpetuation of 'the multifarious, but outmoded duties which had accumulated over the years'.[37]

The hierarchical nature of the public health department also adversely affected junior MOs. In the 1950s and 1960s local government departments were organized around functions with a professional as head, but, as Stewart has recently remarked, professionalism sat uneasily with bureaucratic hierarchy.[38] Dr J. Kershaw, one of the few MOsH to advocate social medicine,[39] noted perceptively that the passing of district health and welfare services to county councils in 1948 had resulted in a dangerous distancing between 'the practical worker and the administrative chief' and a greater tendency towards hierarchical, bureaucratic and authoritarian admini-

stration.[40] The county district group of MOsH warned in 1951
that those district MOsH serving as divisional MOs should
ideally be appointed advisors to area sub-committees with real
powers. Otherwise they would effectively be assistants to the
county medical officer, which would involve a degree of
'subordination' that no doctor would welcome and which
would make recruitment to the field difficult.[41] Writing in
Public Health, Dr H.K. Cowan advised district MOs to resist
'encroachment' by the county. While generally in favour of
'mixed' appointments, he was very much opposed to divisional
schemes which in his opinion did not often result in sufficient
decentralization of the county's responsibilities.[42] The hierarchical nature of the public health service was further
exemplified by the way in which promotions were gained only
by waiting for 'dead men's shoes'. Warren and Cooper noted
that the top jobs of county and county borough MOsH were
invariably filled by the man who had been the deputy.[43] It was
expected that all MOsH would have worked their way up
through the ranks and councils obviously tended to appoint
from within the local department regardless of merit in the
manner condemned by Jameson and Picken in 1936.[44]

From early on MOsH recognized both the need for local
government reform and the fact that the future of the public
health service was bound up with that of the local authorities.[45]
However, central government left the initiative to the local
authorities who were hopelessly split on the issue: the
Association of Municipal Corporations wanted the extension
of single-purpose authorities, while the other four associations
(the County Council's Association, the Urban District
Councils' Association, the Rural District Councils' Association and the Association of Parish Councils) all favoured the
retention of the existing system with some reconsideration of
the position of conurbations and of county/district boundaries. As Alexander has recently pointed out, such a conflict
was the inevitable product of the institutionalization of vested
urban and rural interests.[46] The Local Government Act 1958,
which authorized the delegation of health and welfare
functions to district authorities, laid down no firm principles
regarding county council and county borough boundaries.
Thereafter the Local Government Commission was given the

job of revising these, while the revision of district boundaries was consigned to county councils.[47] The Commission made slow progress and in some cases the cure appeared to be worse than the disease. The amalgamation of Cambridgeshire and the Isle of Ely provided one of the most notorious examples. Ely had combined its health and welfare departments; in Cambridgeshire they had remained separate. According to the MOH appointed to the new authority (previously the MOH for Cambridgeshire), no advice was taken from chief officers and, in the new authority of just under 300,000 population, there were appointed in addition to himself, two deputies, a principal school medical officer, who also acted as the assistant county MO (previously the MOH for Ely), together with a separate county welfare officer and two deputies, and a children's officer with an assistant and a deputy. In all probability the new MOH was correct in his observation that 'no doubt our masters felt that by doing what they have done, all would have some sort of a bite of the new cake'.[48] Not until 1965 did the minister, Crossman, grasp the nettle of local government reform, and referring to the poor image of local authorities, appointed a royal commission.[49] However, its recommendations were to come too late to permit any realistic consideration of unifying the health service under the auspices of local authorities, a possibility that was in any case fragile because of the financial implications and because of opposition from the medical profession.

In the meantime, recruitment to the field of public health proved difficult. In 1964 it was calculated that while the numbers of GPs had risen by 3,579 (19 per cent) between 1948 and 1959 and that of hospital medical staff by 5,000 (31 per cent), the number of MOsH had fallen by 100.[50] Morale in the service was low, and in 1967 one school medical officer wrote to the BMA's Public Health Committee to say that he had 'the feeling he was a third grade doctor, who, finding a condition needing hospital treatment, referred the patient to the second grade family doctor, who then referred the case to the grade I hospital doctor'.[51] Similarly a county MO wrote to the BMA's Committee bewailing the poor image of the MOH and his association in the public mind with the unlovable figure of Dr Snoddy in the popular TV series, 'Dr Finlay's Casebook'.[52]

This widespread demoralization was also reflected in the activities of the Society of Medical Officers of Health. In 1958 the secretary of the Association of County Medical Officers remarked on the lethargy of MOsH, especially the district MOsH, complaining that the annual conference of public health inspectors seemed to be a more lively and well-attended event than that of the MOsH and that very few MOsH bothered to speak at key events like the Royal Society of Health Congress.[53]

Undoubtedly public health departments in the post-war period could have been more imaginative. As in the 1930s, the range of their activities tended to be narrowly dictated by the acts of Parliament. Injunctions to undertake epidemiological research, for example, were largely ignored. The position of MOsH as employees of local government was difficult, both as doctors, and in terms of working within the structure of local authorities, but the evidence suggests that while resenting the label of 'administrators with medical knowledge', this was not such an inaccurate description of the work of MOsH, who were preoccupied with the delivery of a wide range of community-based health and welfare services and whose regimes often reflected the worst rigidities of the local government bureaucracy.

MOsH AND GPs: NEW PARTNERS?

In the post-war period, the MOH found himself sharing the same extra-hospital territory with the GP (in the mid-1960s, only five MOsH sat on RHBs and only 15 per cent had appointments to hospital staff).[54] In Honigsbaum's view, 'whereas before they [MOsH] had done all they could to keep GPs out of public health work, now they did all they could to bring them in'.[55] This is only superficially correct, for in both periods the relationship was rather more complicated. In the 1920s and 1930s the cry of encroachment raised by the GPs should be understood more in terms of GP pique and public health confidence than as a deliberate effort by MOsH to drive out the GP. In the post-war period, both sectors of the profession were acutely demoralized, but the MOH the more so because he lacked a firm rationale for what he was doing. It is true that senior MOsH increasingly sought to emphasize the way in which local authority services provided the natural complement to general practice, but more in order to provide a niche for the MOH as the co-ordinator of community health services than as a means of bringing the GP into the public health service. Moreover, in many respects MOsH and GPs remained rivals; particularly in terms of the clinical work still undertaken by large numbers of assistant MOs. Academics in the field of public health were sufficiently certain that there was little enough future in what the public health departments were doing to take the lead in advocating a new focus for the senior MOH, involving administration on a broader scale which would allow him to forge a new role that overlapped less with the general practitioner.

In the early 1950s, C.F. Brockington, professor of social and preventive medicine at Manchester, wrote at length about the importance of family medicine and the need to integrate the work of the public health department and the GP around the family unit. He also hoped that such a service would make the need for health centres clear.[56] Sir Andrew Davidson, the chief medical officer for Scotland, agreed that the way forward for the NHS was to emphasize domiciliary health services through the co-operation of the family doctor and the MOH. He saw this as a logical development: in the nineteenth century the public health service had focused its attention on environmental issues; and in the early twentieth century, on personal health services, through the clinics which served those people (primarily mothers and children) not covered by national health insurance. After the introduction of the NHS, which guaranteed universal access to GP services, he felt it should be possible for both the GP and public health service to concentrate on the development of family medicine.[57] Brockington's language in particular echoed that of the founders of the Peckham Health Centre, whose pioneering experiment he believed had shown the importance of fostering family health. Physicians made a substantial contribution to the post-war literature on the importance of 'rebuilding the family'. For example, in an influential lecture given in 1946, Dr J.C. Spence, a paediatrician, defined the purpose of the family as ensuring growth and physical health, giving the right scope for emotional experience, preserving the art of motherhood and teaching behaviour.[58] MOsH played a major role in identifying so-called 'problem families' in the 1940s and 1950s, which fed into current anxieties regarding the prevalence of juvenile delinquency.

Government reports of the early 1950s also extolled the idea of family medicine. The Guillebaud Report on the costs of the NHS commented: 'Increasingly it is in the home, the family, and the everyday way of life where we may have to look for the basic deficiencies which are leading to ill-health.'[59] In many respects these sentiments were similar to those expressed by Newman in the 1930s, but the context in terms of the structure of the health services was very different. No longer did the MOH feel that he was in the vanguard of state medicine. Left with a variety of health and welfare services to administer, his relationship to the new NHS was far from clear. The GP, on the other hand, appeared to have emerged from 1948 in a position of strength, his status as an independent contractor intact. However, as the Collings Report showed, large numbers of GPs lacked the proper facilities to practise.[60] The Report painted a very bleak picture of general practice in Britain, citing numerous instances of GP surgeries without even a washbasin or examination couch. Titmuss for one was suspicious of the author's research methodology,[61] but there was enough truth in the Report to indicate that the standards of general practice had reached a very low ebb. The ideas of Brockington and Davidson could thus be made to serve a double purpose: to provide GPs with much needed backup from domiciliary services and a rationale for the services administered by the public health department. It was recognized that the separation of the three parts of the health service could prove problematic. The Guillebaud Report, for example, laid particular emphasis on the need to mitigate the effects of separation on the maternity services and suggested that any practical schemes of co-operation between general practitioners and MOsH would be welcome.[62]

Both the BMA and the Society of Medical Officers of Health agreed that the most likely vehicle for achieving such co-operation was the health visitor. Section 24 of the NHS Act had

in effect called for health visitors to give medico-social advice
to families in need of health education, domiciliary care and
aftercare, and it was therefore logical that she should work in
close contract with the GP.[63] In 1954 a document issued by the
BMA and Society of Medical Officers of Health urged co-
operation between health visitors and GPs based on the
philosophy of family medicine:

The general practitioner is primarily responsible for the health of the
individual and the family, while the health and welfare of the family in
relation to the community is a responsibility of the medical officer of health
and his staff. The close association of all concerned, as members of one team,
is of vital importance if these responsibilities are to be adequately fulfilled.[64]

In 1960 the Joint Working Party of the College of General
Practitioners and the Royal College of Nursing emphasized
that the MOH should take the initiative in promoting co-
operation.[65]

Many MOsH took this idea very seriously. In 1968 Hinks
documented a large number of projects promoting integration
between GPs and MOsH and between hospitals and MOsH,[66]
but such attempts are nevertheless difficult to quantify. For
example, it was certainly not uncommon for a hospital to build
a new day centre for the elderly and only then to let the local
authority know its transport requirements, something that
required lengthy planning on the part of the local authority.
Nor was it uncommon for GPs to have only the haziest idea as
to the remit of the public health department.[67] Perhaps the idea
for co-operation between GPs and MOsH which attracted
most attention, and for which some quantifiable data are
available, was that of attaching health visitors to general
practitioners. The MOsH of Cardiff and Oxford were the first
to take this step in 1962. Attachment schemes received
considerable praise, but were administratively difficult to work
out and progress was slow. By 1967 only 11 per cent of health
visitors were attached.[68] In fact, there is some doubt as to how
far such schemes achieved genuine integration between public
health and general practitioner services. In the case of health
visitor attachment, health visitors themselves were not usually
consulted and resented the fact that GPs often tried to use
them as general dogsbodies rather than treating them as equal

partners in the primary health care team. Many GPs were very slow to appreciate the work of the health visitor, preferring the district nurse, whose work was more easily subject to direction. In Buckinghamshire, M. Jefferys found some GPs looking back nostalgically to the days when the district nurse was the only 'social service'.[69] In 1963 only 25 per cent of general practitioners were prepared to accept attached health visitors compared with 54 per cent who would accept district nurses and midwives.[70] On the local authority side, the Association of Municipal Corporations made it clear that it did not relish the idea of attachment as effective secondment, obviously having no desire to meet a bill for services controlled by general practitioners.[71] One recent evaluation of health visiting has suggested that the reason attachment schemes were endorsed so strongly by central government was because they were perceived as cost-effective methods of delivering primary health care.[72] Certainly some MOsH voiced suspicions as to how far attachment schemes were welcomed as a means of supporting GPs and thereby of diverting attention from a more thoroughgoing examination of the parlous state of general practice.[73] Health visitor attachment schemes were in any case but a small step towards integrating the community health services; however, the suspicion of GPs added to the practical difficulties faced by MOsH in negotiating the financial and administrative aspects of the schemes and meant that progress was slow.

In many respects the secretary of the Association of County Medical Officers of Health was correct when he pointed out in 1957 that effective co-ordination of the community health services was impossible without administrative integration,[74] but that raised the old spectre of local authority control and a salaried service. In particular, GPs were very suspicious of any move by local authorities to build health centres. In 1946 MOsH had hoped that health centres would prove their salvation by allowing them to co-ordinate community health services. However few centres were built prior to 1966. The reasons are complex. In the first instance central government refused to bear the cost of the capital spending programme, but the medical politics were much more complicated than this: the BMA was suspicious of local authority control; the executive councils, which controlled general practice after 1946, had no planning capacity; and the regional hospital boards, which might have promoted the setting-up of diagnostic centres, had no incentives to do so. Hall *et al.* have pointed out that the concept of the health centre was essentially vague.[75] In the 1940s centres were promoted as a means of integrating the NHS, but as Sir George Godber commented in 1960, little genuine co-operation between the public health and general practitioner services took place in the few that were built in the post-war years. He concluded that 'health centres have proved an expensive method of providing capital for better accommodation for general practice'.[76] The 1962 Report on the medical services sponsored by the Royal Colleges, the BMA and the Society of Medical Officers of Health recommended against building more health centres and agreed that to all intents and purposes GP and local authority services had existed independently in the same building.[77] A report of the Medical Practitioners Union (MPU), issued in 1960, documented GPs' lack of commitment to the existing centres, for fear that they might lead to a full-salaried service and that other GPs in the area might benefit if patients decided to transfer to the new premises. On the whole, the MPU report found GPs ill-informed about local authority services and about the literature on health centres.[78] In Bristol, where the William Budd Health Centre was one of the more successful ventures, the MOH undertook an extremely complicated and time-consuming series of informal negotiations with all the GPs before the proposal was formally presented.[79] The building of centres boomed in the later 1960s, only when the interest of central government revived, seeing them this time as a means of promoting community care. GPs were won over by the favourable financial terms they were offered as an inducement to use health centre premises (included as part of the GPs' Charter of 1966), in conjunction with the difficulty of raising the large loans necessary for establishing group practices.[80]

The issue of health centres showed the difficulties faced by the MOH in assuming the role of co-ordinator of community health services. In fact, the whole question of 'encroachment' was far from dead and the GP and the MOH each trod warily round the preserves of the other. One MOH even went so far as to express the opinion that relations between the two groups had been better in the 1930s.[81] On balance this is unlikely to have been the case, but the workings of the school medical service provide a good example of the tensions that continued to exist between the two groups of doctors. In 1950 the BMA and the Society of Medical Officers of Health agreed that MOs would refer children to specialists only after consulting the family doctor and giving him the opportunity of making all further arrangements. An inquiry the following year found great dissatisfaction among school medical officers, many of whom complained that GPs failed to appreciate the value of the school medical service. The MOH for Middlesborough commented bitterly, 'The older GPs view us with a certain amount of suspicion tinged with pity and contempt felt by the well-paid for the indigent.'[82]

GPs continued to threaten to take over the work of all MOs involved in local authority clinics. The volume of clinic work declined very considerably after 1948; attendance at ante-natal clinics, for example, fell by 21 per cent between 1944 and 1955. MOsH recognized this to be an inevitable result of the universal access to GP services provided by the NHS, yet they remained critical of the GPs' interest in and capacity to do the work. Reviewing the state of the maternity services in 1956, the MOH for Dorset insisted that local authority clinics provided an essential adjunct to GP services through their education programmes, particularly in mothercraft, a fact that many GPs 'failed, and often stubbornly refuse, to recognize'.[83]

Nevertheless, there was a difference between the interests of the assistant MOs, who did the clinic work, and the higher grades of public health doctors, which led to a certain lack of sympathy on the part of senior MOsH for the position of their colleagues. The public health journals recognized that MOs who did not want to take on administrative responsibilities had no career structure.[84] A majority (60 per cent) of assistant MOs were women[85] who did mainly maternal and child welfare work and had done so since the inter-war period, when it provided one of the few available jobs for women in medicine. They could hope to rise only to the grade of senior MO, or much more infrequently principal MO. Yet in 1962 the incoming president of the Society of Medical Officers of Health admitted to having always felt that public health doctors should all aim to become full MOsH, a somewhat unrealistic goal in view of the small number of jobs at the top.[86]

Academics and government reports also consistently prophesied an end to the job of clinical medical officer. Professor J.N. Morris, who has been a leading proponent of social medicine and who was later to be influential in formulating the role of the community physician, argued in a Chadwick Trust Lecture in 1957 that prevention and cure should be integrated in the work of the GP.[87] In 1959 the Cranbrook Report on maternity services deemed the work of local authorities in this area to be superfluous. *Public Health* accepted that obstetrics was now a specialty, arguing only that the local authority should continue to provide a place for GP obstetricians to do ante-natal work.[88] Four years later the Gillie Report on the family doctor predicted that GPs would participate more fully in the clinical work of the local health department, 'replacing many of the full-time doctors in those departments'.[89] A similar line was taken by the Sheldon Report on child health in the late 1960s[90] and was also implicit in NHS reorganization in 1974. But the clinical medical officers continue to practise to this day, the significant difference being that since 1974 the gulf between them and the community physicians has become much wider and the problem of an inadequate career structure much more acute.[91]

From the early 1960s it was obvious that academics, central government and senior public health doctors were not convinced that a firm base could be built for public health that included clinical work. The MOH for Hampshire probably spoke for a large number of his colleagues when he stated firmly to the Association of County Medical Officers that he 'really thought the functions of those officers would to a large extent disappear'.[92] As a natural corollary he was prepared wholeheartedly to promote the role of the GP in clinical prevention by providing for him as full a set of backup services as possible:

The various domiciliary services which a local health authority is called upon to provide by the NHS Act are intended to be used by the family doctor, they should be his to command, an integral part of his armamentarium for providing care for his patient.[93]

He did not fear encroachment, seeing the role of the MOH as being primarily administrative and would have agreed with the GP giving a Chadwick Trust Lecture in 1961, who argued that the GP should do the work of clinical prevention and the MOH act as the salaried public health advisor to the local executive council.[94] The *Medical Officer* saw something attractive in the prospect of the GP taking over the clinical work, wondering if this would not then allow the MOH to emerge 'as a coordinator and overseer of the health services of his community' rather than being 'confined to the administration of the smallest part of them'.[95]

The journal was by no means alone in thinking that the answer might be to broaden the MOH's administrative role and make it the basis for specialization in the field. As early as 1954, Dr E.D. Irvine, the MOH for Manchester, urged public health doctors to think more positively about administration. While deploring the idea that MOsH were but 'administrators with medical knowledge', he pointed out that the idea of some town clerks that MOsH should only give advice and not have any executive administrative functions was also dangerous. He disagreed with Parry's view[96] that the new order gave MOsH the chance to cut the 'Gordian knot' of administration and devote themselves to epidemiology and prevention: 'In my judgment, unless the doctor controls the organisation he cannot hope to be effective in his role as epidemiologist.'[97] In fact, a pamphlet put out by the Society of Medical Officers of Health in 1954 on the functions of the MOH fell just short of claiming the right to administer all local health and welfare services.[98]

Other sections of the medical profession also recognized that administration posed a problem. The analysis of the president of the Royal College of Physicians came close to that of Irvine:

The dilemma confronting almost every profession is whether its members shall concentrate on strictly professional work and lose the power to direct it, or learn administration so as to be able to remain in control of it, thus losing the time to practise it.[99]

Behind statements such as this was the growing realization that the NHS was a complex system requiring not only day-to-day administration but fundamental decision-making that would in turn affect the work of doctors. Doctors had to decide whether to get involved.

Academics in departments of public health and social medicine began to push in the late 1950s for courses in medical administration, by which they meant not day-to-day administration but the larger problems of health care delivery. In 1958 Grundy described the trend in public health teaching as moving from the 'traditional' emphasis on sanitary science, public health administration, epidemiology of infectious disease and vital statistics, to the 'intermediate' type of curriculum which added personal health services and health education, and finally to a 'comprehensive' course. This both enlarged the scope of the curriculum and changed its emphasis to include medical sociology; the organization of health and welfare services, medical care and social services; statistics; general epidemiology; personal hygiene and environmental hygiene.[100] More traditional professors of public health were quick to question Grundy's sense of the direction the field was taking. J. Johnstone Jervis declared that he was 'disappointed, disillusioned and disheartened' by it and continued for some years to argue that the primary concern of public health was and should be environmental.[101] He blamed social medicine for diverting public health from its true path. Jervis's arguments were presented in such a way that they sounded at best defensive and at worst reactionary. Certainly, his was a minority opinion among leaders in the field. Nevertheless, many recent commentators on community medicine would argue that he was right to warn MOsH against neglecting their traditional environmental tasks.[102] For in seeking a niche in the new medical universe, public health appeared to be set on putting all or at least most of its eggs in the administrative basket.

Most leaders in the field saw the development of medical administration as promising to give the MOH both specialist status and a more central place in the medical care system. Professor Wofinden was reflecting this view when in 1959 he referred to public health doctors as 'being out of step with this age of medical specialization' and urged them to plan for a future not in a 'subservient executive role within social administrations' but rather as 'broad advisors' to the health service.[103] Dr J. Mackintosh, one of the very few clinical medical officers to play a leading role in the Society of Medical Officers of Health, moved from seeing (in 1955) the future of the clinic doctors as 'social physicians', concentrating on community clinical medicine and outreach to families, to hoping (by the end of the decade) that they would become local medical administrators.[104] However, leaders in the field had not allowed room for the clinical medical officer in their new concept of training for the MOH. Rather, it was assumed that these doctors would cease to practise as GPs took over the work of clinical prevention.

By the mid-1960s this vision was being more clearly articulated. M.D. Warren, a senior lecturer in preventive and social medicine at the London School of Hygiene, wrote about the need to separate the clinical and administrative strands in public health: 'For the future we want to graft preventive medicine onto curative medicine [in the shape of the GP], link community medicine with institutional medicine [by relocating the remaining clinic doctors in hospitals] and develop the specialty of medical administration.'[105] In 1962 the recommendations of the Porritt Report on the organization of medical services made it all the more urgent for the MOH to be trained properly to occupy a specialized niche. The Report advocated the unification of health services under the area health boards, which would delegate the work of administering the personal preventive health services to 'departments of social health' based in the principal hospital of the area. Thus the Report also envisaged a link between the remaining clinical medical officers and the hospital. However, the role of the MOH remained shadowy. The Report talked only of one or more consultants to departments of social health who 'might well be recruited from among existing MOsH' and who would advise the local authorities on environmental health.[106] The idea of the MOH as specialist advisor went down well enough, but both MOsH and the Ministry of Health rightly feared that the hospitals would dominate in such a structure,[107] and academics knew that to attain consultant status the MOH had to be trained to advise on more than environmental health.

In an influential article on the future of the family doctor, published at the height of the 'crisis' over general practice, Titmuss fuelled debate about the future of the MOH by asking whether, if the GP became more of a community doctor, there would still be a place for the MOH.[108] Dr J.J.A. Reid, the MOH for Northamptonshire, immediately replied that the answer was to train the MOH in medical administration and transform him into a specialist whose knowledge and techniques would be available to his colleagues in all branches of medicine. Like Wofinden, Reid wanted to make the MOH a 'broad advisor' to the health service.[109] Reid was exceptional among MOsH in taking up the call for a new training and a new role; he went on to become a leading advocate of community medicine and the community physician. Many MOsH were dissatisfied with the training provided by the diploma in public health,[110] but there was no overwhelmingly enthusiastic response to the new focus on medical administration. Administration continued to be understood by most in terms of organization and methods. Furthermore, the clinical medical officers, who formed the majority of doctors working in public health departments, did not consider their work to be primarily administrative.

The first diploma in medical services administration was offered in 1959 by the Department of Social Medicine at Edinburgh. In a letter to the *Lancet*, the Department's professor of social medicine, S.L. Morrison, linked medical administration to social medicine, arguing that it involved the practice of medicine in relation to population and groups rather than individuals.[111] In 1966 the Royal College of Physicians defined social medicine as comprising both epidemiology and the study of the needs of society;[112] Morrison was following the second of these strands when he suggested that medical administration was effectively the practice of social medicine. The course at Edinburgh aimed to train doctors in 'community diagnosis' and included epidemiology, statistics, medical sociology, preventive medicine and economics, politics and the law in relation to health problems in the community. As such it closely resembles Grundy's 'comprehensive' model for public health education. By 1967 the Royal College of Physicians had given their blessing to the hope that in the future 'senior medical administrators' would be 'more clearly equated with consultants'[113] and a working party set up by the Nuffield Provincial Hospitals Trust on training in medical administration took as given the idea that 'ultimately' clinical work would go to the GPs and the hospitals, and for the first time linked the work of the MOH in medical administration to that of the administrators employed by the hospital boards.[114] The reorganization of the NHS in 1974 would make the idea of separating senior public health doctors from clinical medical officers a reality and would also fuse together the work of medical officers of health and medical officers employed by the hospital boards.

There was little hope of the MOH becoming the lynch-pin in preventive clinical medicine when the NHS provided universal access to GP services and when successive government reports sought to prop up the ailing GP by advocating that he become the leader of the community health team. Academics sought to secure the public health doctor a niche by developing the concept of medical administration and raising the MOH to specialist status. The future of the clinic doctor was not seriously discussed. However, the precise nature of the role envisaged for the MOH was far from clear and would not become so until the late 1960s when J.N. Morris fleshed out the concept of the community physician. Even then, confusion would remain as to whether the community physician was intended to be primarily an advisor or a manager. It is noticeable that while E.D. Irvine stressed the importance of an executive role in his discussion of medical administration in 1954, by the mid-1960s the emphasis had shifted very much towards the acquisition of administrative skills as a means to enabling the MOH to fill the role of 'broad advisor'.

It is not clear that the push to transform the role of the MOH would have succeeded had not the Seebohm Committee's recommendations for changing the way social work was organized in local government[115] made fundamental restructuring imperative. The Seebohm Report on the future of the personal and allied social services recommended that all social work be removed from the public health departments and that separate departments of social services be set up. This threatened to remove the fastest-growing part of the MOH's empire and to destroy his attempt to establish a role as the administrator and co-ordinator of community health services.

MOsH AND SOCIAL WORKERS: A DIVORCE?

Social work services had grown enormously in the post-war years. As Titmuss noted in 1956,[116] committees of inquiry on children, adoption, rehabilitation, mental illness, marriage and divorce, after-care of discharged prisoners, health visitors, district nurses, and on social work itself had all recommended the employment of more social workers. Local authorities employed social workers in the health, welfare, children's, housing and education departments to work primarily with children, the mentally ill, the chronically ill, the physically handicapped and the elderly. Inevitably, there was overlap between departments, and in 1954 D. Donnison's study of the neglected child exposed the confusion in local government social work services to its first sustained criticism.[117] Despite the rapid increase in the number of social workers, no review of their organization (as opposed to social workers themselves) was undertaken until the Seebohm Inquiry

One of the major issues prior to the Seebohm Inquiry was whether the health and welfare departments of the local authority should be merged under the control of the MOH. The Society of Medical Officers of Health's booklet on the functions of the MOH, published in 1954, asked that the MOH be placed in 'a position of authority' in respect to all matters bearing on social medicine, which raised the ire of other local authority workers.[118] The *Local Government Chronicle*, for example, reviewed the booklet under the heading, 'Ubiquitous Doctors'.[119] In fact, the majority of MOsH were not eager to take on full responsibility for welfare services. What they wanted was a guarantee that they would have a major voice in the way services affecting the disabled, handicapped, chronically and mentally ill and the elderly were organized and how staff were deployed. In 1964 the Society of Medical Officers of Health asked the BMA's Public Health Committee to reword its resolution on the amalgamation of departments, arguing that welfare duties were 'not in the strict sense of the word, a "legitimate" duty of the MOH' and that policy would be better expressed in the following:

The Committee favours the closest possible coordination of health and welfare services, even to the extent of combining their administration in one department and considers that the administration of the welfare services should be regarded as work which might properly and advantageously be undertaken by a medical officer of health.[120]

While MOsH did not wish to renounce their interest in absorbing the work that welfare departments carried out under the National Assistance Act 1948 (there were large areas of overlap, especially in respect to the elderly and handicapped), they had three main reasons for treading warily. In the first place some admitted to finding the work essentially 'tiresome and difficult';[121] second, the assumption of these responsibilities was perceived to drive them more firmly 'into the local authority camp';[122] and last but not least was the fact that they did not usually receive any additional remuneration when departments of health and welfare were combined.[123]

In general the debate over the organization of local government departments was conducted without much reference to the principles on which such a merger could be justified. Government reports, for example, swung back and forth on the issue of amalgamation depending on what the other concerns were. The Guillebaud Report on the cost of the NHS recommended unification on grounds of greater cost efficiency.[124] In 1967 the Mallaby Report on local government staffing said that MOsH were in too short supply for them to be involved in the administration of welfare departments, but the Maud Report (issued the same year) on management in local government, favoured unified departments, again for the sake of cost efficiency.[125] (This Report was overtaken by the appointment of the Royal Commission on Local Government.)[126] M. Jefferys was one of the few to reach a conclusion based on empirical research rather than administrative or professional convenience. Her research on the social services of Buckinghamshire County Council, where health and welfare were amalgamated, convinced her of the wisdom of this course because of the impossibility of separating socio-medical need;

the bulk of the department's clients were old and a large number also suffered from disability.[127]

It was striking that MOsH were on the whole unable to articulate any sound principle for their involvement in welfare work. MOsH arguing in favour of unification tended merely to assert that the work needed 'medical direction' and, in particular, that the supervision of the MOH was needed to allocate work between health visitors and social workers.[128] R. Huws Jones, the principal of the National Institute for Social Work and a member of the Seebohm Committee, made a point of asking MOsH repeatedly for evidence as to the benefits of joint health and welfare departments when the Committee took evidence. The best that representatives of the Association of County Medical Officers of Health could do was to suggest that the trend towards amalgamation proved its desirability.[129] Huws Jones was seeking concrete evidence as to why a medical doctor should be best placed to direct social work, but MOsH failed to provide it. Indeed individual MOsH found the visits of the Seebohm Committee difficult to handle because they had not given sufficient thought to social work principles. R.W. Elliott, one of the most senior MOsH in the country, reported that the Committee seemed to be only interested in broad principles and were 'not attuned to the minutiae of social work'.[130] MOsH tended to think about day-to-day administrative complexities, while the Seebohm Committee was determined to think in terms of broad-brush reorganization.

In the same year that Donnison's book exposed the confusion of the social work services dealing with children and advocated greater co-ordination using 'key' workers, Titmuss went a step further and advocated a completely different approach to the whole problem of the social services. He argued that individualized inquiries into departments or groups of workers failed to take into account the crucial effect of the administrative setting of the worker, concentrating only on the nature of the work and the quality of the workers.[131] The most characteristic theme of Titmuss's writing thereafter was the need to rationalize boundaries and combine structures. As J. Cooper has pointed out, this theme became more generally popular in the 1960s.[132] By the mid-1960s Titmuss had identified eight principles of structural reform justifying the creation of unified social service departments, which he felt would place the emphasis firmly on the need for services rather than on biological or sociological criteria.[133] Departments would be organized around the provision of services and 'not categories of clients or particular fragments of need'[134] and would provide an environment in which social work could develop as a profession. Titmuss believed that administrative reorganization effecting fundamental structural change was necessary and sufficient to achieve change in the use of resources, in accountability, access and patterns of use. A similar faith in economies of scale and a 'structural fix' also underpinned local governments reform in the 1970s and indeed the reorganization of the NHS in 1974.[135] As B. Abel-Smith subsequently remarked, 'Reorganization was the key to comprehensive social planning and the assertion of rational priorities.'[136] In retrospect it may be argued that one of the most striking failures of the 'structural fix' was the lack of appreciation as to the difficulties of pouring old wine (personnel) into new bottles (rationalized structures).[137]

Titmuss spearheaded the group that was highly influential in pushing the government into setting up the Seebohm Inquiry, whose only medical member was J.N. Morris. However, the original terms of reference of the Seebohm Committee asked it to 'review the organization and responsibilities of the local authority personal social services in England and Wales and to consider what changes are desirable to secure an effective family service'.[138] The emphasis on developing a family service was born of the overwhelming anxieties about juvenile delinquency. The Ingleby Committee on children and young persons, the Scottish Kilbrandon Committee on young people and the Longford Report on crime had all recommended a family social work service.[139] The Seebohm Committee rapidly asserted its determination to interpret its terms of reference widely in order to embrace the possibility of securing comprehensive services for all, irrespective of family membership.[140] However, many MOsH misread the Committee's purpose, and the evidence they gave in 1966 shows that they assumed the intention was to promote the reorganization of social work in order to cope with 'failing families producing juvenile delinquents'. They therefore argued that the aim should be to promote the mental and physical health of all families and that the health visitor should be the key worker (and hence the health department the key department) in securing the health and welfare of the 'normal family'.[141] Titmuss had floated the idea of unified social service departments to a medical audience at the Royal Society of Health Congress in 1965.[142] The failure of MOsH to notice the influential arguments of social scientists regarding trends in social services during the 1960s left them at a considerable disadvantage in understanding the rapid movements in health and social service reform at the end of the decade.

After the event, MOsH and the BMA commented bitterly on the bias of the Committee's membership towards the social work cause. The Committee was certainly both cohesive and authoritative[143] and from the beginning it was influenced by arguments in favour of radical reorganization, which the evidence of the MOsH did nothing to counter. It was clear that the creation of social service departments threatened to reduce the public health service to a rump. However, local health departments were perceived to have failed on three crucial fronts: first and most serious was the charge that they had failed to make sufficient progress in the provision of community care. Both Titmuss and Morris were convinced of the weakness of local authorities in general and of public health in particular in this respect. In two articles published in 1961 Titmuss had argued that the NHS and National Assistance Acts had given local authorities all the legal powers they needed to develop community care and yet they were spending less in real terms in 1959–60 than they had done in 1949–50.[144] This did not necessarily reflect on the MOH directly, although Titmuss clearly felt that MOsH could have shown more imagination and more determination to develop community services.[145] Lack of progress under the Health and Welfare Plan of 1963 was particularly evident.[146] The plan consisted of local authorities' proposals for action in the field of community care over the following decade and was meant to complement the Hospital Plan of the same year. As several authors have commented, there was no attempt to make the Plan compatible with that for the hospitals. Nor was it as 'national' as the Hospital Plan, largely because of the autonomy of local authorities.[147] J.J.A. Reid, always one of the most perceptive commentators among MOsH, saw the Plan as the last hope of salvation for the public health service,[148] but by 1966 there were still large variations in what had been achieved (some idea of these is given in Table 1). Rehin, Houghton and Martin's study of mental health social work in five areas concluded that the training given mental welfare officers was often slight and that progress could be described as at best 'uneven'.[149] The *Medical Officer* fiercely rejected the idea that local health departments had been dragging their feet,[150] but many of the replies to the survey on issues relating to the Seebohm Inquiry carried out by the Association of County Medical Officers of Health in 1966, provided evidence of the use of relatively untrained staff and the 'doubling up' of welfare officers and mental welfare officers.[151] Trained staff were, of course, in very short supply, but it was not clear that MOsH always appreciated the importance of trained social workers. In 1962 one MOH complained of mental health work being 'grabbed' by social workers.[152]

The second charge against local health departments was that during the post-war period MOsH had for the most part demonstrated a lack of sympathy with the work and aspirations of social workers. Both main public health journals reacted angrily in 1959 to the Younghusband Report on social work, which recommended the appointment of three kinds of social workers—the trained, the generalist and the welfare assistant.[153] The public health journals suggested that such a structure sought to create a 'mystique' about social work when its practice was obviously merely a matter of common sense.[154] However, *Public Health* did admit that:

In a properly integrated service for health, welfare and social care, what the Report has to say would make admirable sense, even if it is sometimes said in rather a lot of words. In a disunited and fragmented service, in which too much jealous attention is paid to who works under whom and too little to who works with whom, the quick and literal implementation of the Working Party's findings could make well chaos worse confounded.[155]

Such a frank confession of the overlapping and hierarchical nature of local authority social work may be read as adequate confirmation of the need for the kind of radical reorganization

Table 1: Status of services provided by selected local authorities, 1962 and 1965 (no. per 1000 population)

local public health department	training centre places for mentally subnormal adult		juvenile		homes for the elderly		health visitors		home helps		social workers	
	1962	1965	1962	1965	1962	1965	1962	1965	1962	1965	1962	1965
Bournemouth CB	0.67	0.40	0.00	0.26	19.4	17.6	0.11	0.14	0.39	0.62	0.12	0.12
Oxford CB	0.28	0.17	0.32	0.32	26.8	31.0	0.10	0.14	0.49	0.55	0.10	0.14
Reading CB	0.41	0.40	0.46	0.44	18.7	21.6	0.10	0.13	0.82	0.67	0.11	0.09
Kingston upon Hull CB	0.66	0.67	0.45	0.45	21.2	24.1	0.13	0.12	0.81	0.86	0.09	0.12
Wolverhampton CB	1.08	0.80	0.51	0.83	20.3	27.0	0.11	0.15	0.39	0.47	0.07	0.08
Durham CC	0.01	0.30	0.24	0.33	11.8	10.3	0.11	0.11	0.71	1.05	0.03	0.05
Yorks. N. Riding CC	0.31	0.15	0.22	0.33	16.2	14.2	0.10	0.10	0.35	0.51	0.05	0.06
Yorks. W. Riding CC	0.43	0.43	0.38	0.42	13.3	12.7	0.09	0.11	0.56	0.68	0.07	0.07
Lincs. Pts. Holland CC	0.00	0.33	1.06	0.72	22.7	23.6	0.10	0.05	0.29	0.30	0.09	0.07
Bucks. CC	0.10	0.27	0.45	0.38	23.7	15.0	0.08	0.06	0.26	0.34	0.05	0.05
England and Wales	0.34	0.32	0.35	0.39	16.1	15.6	0.11	0.12	0.55	0.63	0.06	0.05

Source: P.P. Cmnd. 1973, 1962–3, xxi, p.265, 'The Development of Community Care: Plans for the Health and Welfare Services of the Local Authorities in England and Wales', and Cmnd. 3022, 1966–7, lviii, p.555, 'The Development of Community Care: Revision to 1975–76 to Plans for the Health and Welfare Services in England and Wales'.

proposed by Seebohm almost a decade later. However, MOsH had little time for any scheme of reorganization that did not leave them in control. From the time of the Younghusband Report onwards MOsH claimed repeatedly that health visitors were the primarily all-purpose social workers. The Young-husband Working Party was not permitted to discuss the role of the health visitor, which was a pity because the Jameson Report on health visiting issued in 1956 had not made up its mind whether the health visitor's work should be primarily medical or social.[156] However, the argument of MOsH that the health visitor was the general purpose social worker, repeated to the Seebohm Committee, showed that the MOH had little appreciation of the nature of social work. Indeed, Dr C.D.L. Lycett, the MOH for Wiltshire, prepared a paper on the relations between MOsH and social workers for the Association of County MOsH in 1964, which was remarkably patronizing:

Those who practise or intend to practise social work are imbued with the desire to establish it as a profession in itself. It is probable that this desire is now being fostered in health department social workers, such as the mental welfare officers . . . . This feeling of entity as a calling and enthusiasm to establish a new profession, is, of course, not confined to social work. In fact, there is now a proliferation of 'professions' probably unknown in previous times, ranging within our own sphere from chiropodists to health education officers, from home help organisers to speech therapists . . . . There is a naive belief that if social workers rather than the MOH had direct access to them, committees could readily be convinced both of the need for and the effectiveness of more social work with resulting sweeping changes in policy and unloosening the purse-strings.[157]

Third in the catalogue of failure of the public health departments was the belief on the part of social scientists and social workers that medical practice in the field of social work left a good deal to be desired. The lack of training of many mental welfare officers was one major cause of concern, but work with 'problem families' provides a perhaps more dramatic example of the distance between the medical and social work approach. Pioneering studies of problem families were carried out in the mid-1940s by MOsH in conjunction with the Eugenics Society. As C.P. Blacker, the head of the Eugenics Society, explained, there had been renewed discussion of the social problem group (a discovery of the 1930s linked to concern about the number of mental defectives and the decline in the national intelligence) as a result of the experience of evacuation, but the idea of a group was quickly displaced by the 'problem family', reflecting 'a transition from an impersonal sociological to a personal and human approach'.[158] This was an *ex post facto* rationalization. In fact, the studies directed by MOsH and published in the mid-1940s still firmly emphasized mental defect as the major cause of family failure, which had also been feared to be the chief characteristic of the 1930s social problem group. Many of the descriptions in the studies used very crude animal imagery and implied that such families were incapable of leading a 'normal' family life.[159]

The Women's Group on Public Welfare (the authors of a famous study of children evacuated during World War II)[160] criticized what they viewed as the confusion of intellectual and mental defect in these studies, arguing that 'problem mothers' were certainly appallingly ignorant, but that most appeared genuinely to love their children, who, whilst improperly cared for, seemed also to love their parents.[161] These were not the affectionless families that, according to Bowlby's theories, produced juvenile delinquents. And where there was affection, it was argued that it should prove possible to educate mothers to a more mature understanding of their duties.

By the late 1940s social workers were de-emphasizing the medical and eugenic passion for classifying and enumerating the characteristics of problem families. The family casework approach pioneered by the Pacifist Service Units during the war and their successors, the Family Service Units, stressed the importance of respecting clients and helping them to achieve their full potential as parents without imposing the case-worker's own standards on them. Titmuss drew attention to the differences between the medical and social work approach, characterizing the former as administrative and the latter as psycho-social.[162]

An editorial in the *BMJ* published in 1966 clearly indicated that the medical profession as a whole was unwilling to accept social workers as equal members of a professional team:

the transfer of administration of medical and quasi-medical functions to the overlordship of a non-medical person may well be thought repugnant to the principle of freedom and independence of the medical profession and a threat to ethical standards.[163]

A note sent to Titmuss in 1967, probably from Morris, opined that 'in the case of the MOsH mutual misunderstanding with social workers has gone so far as to be a major factor in the [Seebohm] Committee's overall thinking on the future shape of the social services'.[164]

Nor was Titmuss any more optimistic about the GP's capacity to undertake the responsibility for social work. In his 1965 article on the role of the family doctor in relation to the social services, Titmuss criticized the Gillie Report on the future of the GP, published in 1963,[165] for providing no evidence to substantiate its claim that GPs were increasingly becoming the co-ordinators, mobilizers, directors, stage managers and leaders in community care.[166] While questioning the actual amount of effort made by GPs in this field, Titmuss also suggested that unified social service departments would provide a means of lifting the burden from overworked GPs. Dr R.W. Elliott, who, as MOH for the West Riding, had played a leading role in instigating schemes of health visitor attachment and in building health centres, was genuinely puzzled by Titmuss's thinking. He wrote to the *Lancet*:

I still do not follow how we can support general medical practice by removing the one man who can help the GP in his professional work . . . . It is surely obvious that the GP and the MOH have one all important common bond—the care of the community health in its natural setting—at home, at work and at play.[167]

But what was needed, in Titmuss's view, were strong social service departments that would be able to stand up to the medical profession. Thus in a reformed and rationalized community health and social service structure built around the social worker and the GP there was no place for the MOH in the role he had been playing since 1948.

While the social work lobby was the immediate cause of the break-up of the local public health departments, it may be argued that such rationale as they had developed for their work was significantly undermined when the NHS Act failed to adopt the public health model for the delivery of personal health services. During the 1950s, public health was demoralized, but general practice was also weak and MOsH did their best to forge a role as the co-ordinators and administrators of community health services. However, as academic leaders in the public health field recognized, their position was fragile and their work did nothing to enhance their standing as doctors, allowing them to be dismissed as 'administrators with medical knowledge'. While academics tried to push public health training in the direction of a broader concept of medical administration, the power of the social work lobby grew. The logic on the one hand of strengthening the GP and promoting him as the focus of the preventive community health services and, on the other, of promoting social workers and social service departments as the means of developing community care, proved the downfall of the MOsH and the public health departments. Local health departments were singularly isolated during the post-war period. As N. Deakin has remarked, local government departments during this period tended to develop 'powerful and exclusive cultures'.[168] Dealing with the complexities of the local authority structure and hierarchy absorbed a major part of the MOH's energies and it seems that many were not sufficiently aware of the importance of thinking—on matters such as social work—that were being developed outside local government circles. Furthermore, there seems to have been very little contact with academics in the field, a legacy of the rupture between public health and social medicine. This was particularly damaging in view of the fact that some of the leading proponents of social medicine, such as Titmuss and Morris, continued to play a significant role in promoting the structure reform of health and social services in the 1960s and 1970s.

NOTES

1. A. Walker, 'The meaning and social division of community care', in *Community Care*, ed A. Walker (Oxford: Blackwell, 1982), p. 17.

2. R. Means and R. Smith, *The Development of Welfare Services for Elderly People* (London: Croom Helm, 1985), p. 167.
3. Walker, 'The meaning and social division of community care', p. 17.
4. M. Brown, 'The development of local authority welfare services from 1948–1965 under pt. III of the National Assistance Act 1948', unpub. Ph.D. thesis, University of Manchester, 1972.
5. See above, p. 48.
6. 'The scope of epidemiology', editorial, *Medical Officer*, 89 (1953), p. 36.
7. 'The Health Congress', *ibid.*, pp. 210–11, comments of Dr J.F. Warin and Dr W. Dodd.
8. J.M. Mackintosh, 'The way ahead', *Public Health*, 68 (1954), p. 4.
9. J.M. Clayton, 'Prevention or cure', *Public Health*, 64 (1951), p. 40.
10. D.E. Parry Pritchard, 'The way ahead', *ibid.*, p. 170.
11. 'The public health service', editorial, *Medical Officer*, 85 (1951), p. 144.
12. BMA Archives, Public Health Committee, 1950–1, Item 1245, Doc. 20, 'Arbitration Case before the Industrial Court', October 1950.
13. *ibid.*, 1957–8, Item 1057, Doc. 36, 'Draft Memo of Evidence for Submission to the Royal Commission on Doctors' and Dentists' Remuneration', pp. 9–10.
14. Association of County Medical Officers of Health Records, Wellcome Institute for the History of Medicine (hereafter CMO), A19, The Association of County Medical Officers of Health of England and Wales, Evidence, nd. fol. 1131.
15. M.D. Warren and J. Cooper, 'Local government medical staff', *Medical Officer*, 118 (1967), p. 186.
16. CMO, A19, 'Medical officers of health in the public health service' by Sir Allen Daley, 1958.
17. M.D. Warren and J. Cooper, 'The medical officer of health: the job, the man and the career', *Medical Officer*, 116 (1966), pp. 41–50.
18. Warren and Cooper, 'Local government medical staff', p. 188.
19. G.F. Bramley, 'Local government medical officers', *Public Health*, 74 (1960), pp. 323–9.
20. 'The future home of public health medicine', editorial, *Medical Officer*, 100 (1958), p. 124.
21. 'One or two tiers?', editorial, *Medical Officer*, 90 (1953), p. 36.
22. Warren and Cooper, 'The medical officer of health', p. 44.
23. W.A. Robson, *Local Government in Crisis* (London: Allen & Unwin, 1966), p. 70.
24. BMA Archives, Public Health Committee, 1951–2, Item 1271, Doc. 5, Meeting of the Public Health Committee, Case of Dr J. Sims-Roberts, 1952.
25. P.P. 'Report of the Committee of Inquiry into the Cost of the NHS', Cmd. 9663, 1955–6, xx, 833, paras 714–15.
26. 'Dr X, 1910–48: Sketch of a medical officer', *Medical Officer*, 99 (1958), p. 21.
27. See below, p. 82 *et seq.*
28. J.D. Stewart, 'The functioning and management of local authorities,' in *Half a Century of Municipal Decline*, ed M. Loughlin, M.D. Gelfand and

K. Young (London: Allen & Unwin, 1985), p. 101.

29. 'Lay administration in the health service?', editorial, *Medical Officer*, 89 (1953), pp. 62–3.

30. CMO, D158, Society of Medical Officers of Health, 'Management and Administration in the Local Government Service'. Summary of Comments on the Report of an Informal Conference arranged by the Society of Town Clerks, 1968.

31. R.J. Haynes, *Organization Theory and Local Government* (London: Allen and Unwin, 1980).

32. CMO, C141, J. Lyons to G. Ramage, 27/4/66.

33. *ibid.*, M.J. Pleydell to Ramage, 4/4/66.

34. *ibid.*, D.E. Cullington to Ramage, 4/4/66.

35. E. Hughes, 'Administration and organisation of the environmental health services', *Public Health* 75 (1961), p. 147.

36. Ministry of Health, Department of Health for Scotland and Ministry of Education, *An Inquiry into Health Visiting* (London: HMSO, 1956).

37. E. Wilkie, *The History of the Council for the Education and Training of Health Visitors* (London: Allen & Unwin, 1979), p. 50.

38. Stewart, 'The functioning and management of local authorities', p. 101.

39. See above, p. 43.

40. J. Kershaw, 'The happy few', *Public Health*, 70 (1956), p. 5.

41. CMO, A110, Memo, Report by the President of the County District Group, 1951, fol. 59.

42. K. Cowan, 'The place of the county district MOH', *Public Health*, 67 (1954), pp. 62–6.

44. See above, p. 26.

45. 'The Health Congress', *Medical Officer*, 89 (1953), comments of J.F. Warin, p. 211; and P.A. Tyser, 'The county district medical officer: an appraisal', *Public Health*, 71 (1957), p. 5.

46. A. Alexander, 'Structure, centralization and the position of local government', in *Half a Century of Municipal Decline*, pp. 51–2.

47. Robson, *Local Government in Crisis*; P.G. Richards, *Delegation in Local Government: County to District Councils* (London: Allen & Unwin, 1956); C. Pearce, *The Machinery of Change in Local Government, 1888–1974* (London: Allen & Unwin, 1980).

48. CMO, C141, P.A. Tyser to Ramage, 7/4/66.

49. Pearce, *The Machinery of Change in Local Government*, p. 110.

50. BMA Archives, Public Health Committee, 1963–4, Item 927, Doc. 57, 'Draft Memo of Evidence to the Mallaby Committee' by J. Ridell and W. Edgar, 3/7/64.

51. BMA Archives, Public Health Committee, 1966–7, Item 806, Doc. 27, 'The Role of the Public Health Service in the Present Crisis', memo by Dr H. Gordon.

52. BMA Archives, Joint Committee of BMA and Society of Medical Officers of Health, 1966–7, Item 780, 'Social Work and the Community', 1/2/67.

53. Society of Medical Officers of Health Records, Wellcome Unit for the History of Medicine, Oxford (hereafter SMOH), A12, Minutes of the

Council of the Society, meeting of the Borough and County Group with the Council, 25/7/58.
54. Warren and Cooper, 'The medical officer of health'.
55. F. Honigsbaum, *The Division in British Medicine* (London: Kogan Page, 1979), p. 310.
56. C. Fraser Brockington, 'The family fulcrum of the health services', *Medical Officer*, 88 (1952), p. 139.
57. Sir Andrew Davidson, 'The broadening outlook in public health', *ibid.*, pp. 237–9.
58. J.C. Spence, *The Purpose of the Family* (London: Epworth Press, 1947), Convocation Lecture for the National Children's Home, 1946.
59. Cmd. 9663, para 618.
60. J.S. Collings, 'General practice in England today', *Lancet*, I (1950), pp. 555–86.
61. Titmuss Papers, LSE, file 135, marginalia on the Collings Report.
62. Cmd. 9663, paras 621, 631–6.
63. 'Health departments and GP cooperation', editorial, *Medical Officer*, 86 (1952), p. 261.
64. 'The GP and the health visitors', editorial, *Public Health*, 67 (1954), p. 114.
65. CMO, A20, Joint Working Party between the College of GPs and the Royal College of Nursing, 'The Health Visitor and the Family Doctor', 27/10/60.
66. M.D. Hinks, *Working Together* (London: King Edward's Hospital Fund, 1968).
67. Interview, DMO, York, 10/4/84.
68. 'Attachment and liaison', editorial, *Medical Officer*, 118 (1967), p. 247.
69. M. Jefferys, *Anatomy of the Social Welfare Services* (London: Michael Joseph, 1965), p. 121.
70. J. Robinson, *An Evaluation of Health Visiting* (London: CETHV, 1982), p. 19.
71. BMA Archives, Public Health Committee, 1964–5, Item 948, Doc. 70, Association of Municipal Corporations, 'Local Authority Health Services and the GP'.
72. Robinson, *An Evaluation of Health Visiting*.
73. 'Health visitor attachment', Special Report, *Public Health*, 79 (1964), p. 9.
74. G. Ramage, 'The GP and the local authority public health services', *Medical Officer*, 97 (1957), pp. 31–40.
75. P. Hall, H. Land, R. Parker and A. Webb, *Change, Choice and Conflict in Social Policy* (London: Heinemann, 1975), pp. 277–310.
76. SMOH, C1/II, 1960 Summer School, County Borough Group, Report of the Hon. Sec., 'Health Centres', p. 7.
77. *A Review of the Medical Services of Great Britain* (London: Social Assay for the Medical Services Review Committee, 1962), pp. 66–7.
78. MPU, *Health Centre Report* by Dr J. Sluggett (London: MPU, 1960).
79. MPU, Health Centre Conference, *Report* (London: MPU, 1967), n.p.
80. Hall *et al.*, *Change, Choice and Conflict*, p. 302; and M. Ryan, 'Health

centre policy in England and Wales', *British Journal of Sociology*, 19 (1968), pp. 34–46.

81. CMO, A22, 'The Relations beween GPs and the Health Visitor' by I.A. McDougall, 6/4/62.

82. BMA Archives, Public Health Committee, 1950–1, Item 1210, Doc. 33, 'Report on Replies to an Enquiry regarding the operation of agreement between the BMA and Society of Medical Officers of Health on the School Health Service'.

83. CMO, A15, 'The Maternity Services', 1956, fol. 846.

84. 'Public health salaries', editorial, *Medical Officer*, 105 (1961), p. 69.

85. Warren and Cooper, 'Local government medical staff', p. 185.

86. E. Hughes, 'The place of the medical officer of health in the public health service', *Public Health*, 77 (1962), p. 6.

87. 'Medical care', editorial, *Medical Officer*, 97 (1957), p. 104.

88. 'The Cranbrook Report', editorial, *Public Health*, 73 (1959), pp. 283–84.

89. Ministry of Health, Central Health Services Council, Standing Medical Advisory Committee, *The Field of Work of the Family Doctor* (London: HMSO, 1963), p. 40.

90. Central Health Services Council, Report of the Sub-Committee of the Standing Medical Advisory Committee, *Child Welfare Centres* (London: HMSO, 1967).

91. See below, p. 130.

92. CMO, A22, 'The Relations between the GP and the Health Visitor', I.A. McDougall, 6/4/62.

93. Cited in Royal Society of Health and College of General Practitioners, *The GP and Preventive Medicine* (London: Royal Society of Health, 1966), p. 10.

94. 'GPs and preventive medicine', editorial, *Medical Officer*, 107 (1962), p. 191.

95. 'Towards a measure of care', editorial, *Medical Officer*, 108 (1962), p. 93.

96. Born of pessimism, see above, p. 48.

97. E.D. Irvine, 'Medical administration', *Public Health*, 67 (1954), pp. 172–5.

98. Society of Medical Officers of Health, *The Functions of the Medical Officer of Health* (London: Society of Medical Officers of Health, 1954).

99. BMA Archives, Public Health Committee, 1953–4, Item 1309, Doc. 4, Society of Medical Officers of Health, 'Postgraduate Education in Public Health of Medical Practitioners'.

100. F. Grundy, 'The teaching of social medicine and public health', *Public Health*, 72 (1958), pp. 123–33.

101. J. Johnstone Jervis, 'The teaching of social medicine and public health', *Public Health*, 73 (1958), pp. 29–33.

102. See below, pp. 146–8.

103. R.C. Wofinden, 'Medical administration: the appropriate forms of teaching', *Public Health*, 73 (1959), pp. 343–53.

104. 'The clinical medical officer', editorial, *Medical Officer*, 93 (1955), p. 212; J. Mackintosh, 'Medical administration and training for it',

Medical Officer, 101 (1959), p. 123.

105. M.D. Warren, 'Possible developments in training for community health and medical administration', *Medical Care*, 4 (1966), pp. 177–80.
106. *A Review of the Medical Services in Great Britain*, p .23.
107. 'At the crossroads', editorial, *Medical Officer*, 109 (1963), p. 167.
108. R.M. Titmuss, 'The role of the family doctor today in the context of Britain's social services', *Lancet* I (1965), p. 2.
109. J.J.A. Reid, 'A new public health—the problems and the challenge', *Public Health*, 79 (1965), pp. 183–96.
110. E.g. R.W. Elliott, MOH for the West Riding. See 'Altering the public health structure', editorial, *Medical Officer*, 118 (1967), p. 198.
111. Letter, S.L. Morrison, *Lancet*, I (1965), p. 329.
112. Royal College of Physicians, *Report on Departments of Social and Preventive Medicine* (London: Royal College of Physicians, 1966), p. 8.
113. Royal College of Physicians, Committee on Medical Administration, *Report* (London: Royal College of Physicians, 1966), p. 4.
114. Nuffield Provincial Hospitals Trust, *Vocational Training in Medicine: Reports of Three Working Parties on Vocational Training for the GP, Psychological Services and the Administration of Hospital and Public Health Services* (Oxford: Nuffield Provincial Hospitals Trust, 1967), p. 42.
115. P.P. 'Report of the Committee on Local Authority and Allied Personal Social Services', Cmnd. 3703, 1967–8, xxxii.
116. Titmuss Papers, LSE, file 104, letter to ?, 1956.
117. D. Donnison, *The Neglected Child* (Manchester: Manchester University Press, 1954).
118. Society of Medical Officers of Health, *Functions of the Medical Officer of Health*.
119. 'The medical officer of health and his colleagues', *Medical Officer*, 94 (1955), p. 15.
120. CMO, C76, J.D.J. Harvard, under-secretary, BMA, to G. Ramage, reporting a deputation led by A. Elliot, MOH for Kent, 9/12/64.
121. 'County borough medical officers of health summer school', *Medical Officer*, 100 (1958), p. 72, views of Dr J. Lyon.
122. E. Hughes, 'More medical or more social?', *Public Health*, 74 (1960), p. 343.
123. BMA Archives, Public Health Committee, 1963–4, Item 927, Doc. 38, 'Statement of Additional Remuneration Received by Medical Officers of Health who also Act as Chief Welfare Officers'.
124. Cmd. 9663, para. 606.
125. Ministry of Housing and Local Government, *Report of the Committee on the Staffing of Local Government* (London: HMSO, 1967), para. 212; and *Report of the Committee on Management in Local Government* (London: HMSO, 1967).
126. P.P., 'Report of the Royal Commission on Local Government', Cmnd. 4040, 1969.
127. Jefferys, *Anatomy of Social Services*, p. 312.
128. 'County borough MOsH summer school', *Medical Officer*, 100 (1958),

pp. 71–2, views of Dr R.J. Dodds, MOH for Smethwick; and Hughes, 'More medical or more social?'.

129. CMO, C142, Summary of discussions with representatives of the Association of County Medical Officers of Health, 25/11/66.

130. CMO, C142, R.W. Elliott to Ramage, 26/7/66.

131. Titmuss Papers, LSE, file 96B, 'The Administrative Setting of Social Services: Some Historical Reflections', *Case Conference* (1954).

132. J. Cooper, *The Creation of the British Personal Social Services* (London: Heinemann, 1983), p. 1.

133. *ibid.*, p. 85.

134. Quoted in *ibid.*, p. 63.

135. R.J. Haynes, *Organization Theory and Local Government*.

136. Quoted in H. Glennerster, with N. Korman and F. Marslen Wilson, *Planning for Priority Groups* (London: Heinemann, 1983), p. 14.

137. The phrase is that of R.G.S. Brown, *Reorganizing the NHS: A Case Study in Administrative Change* (Oxford: Blackwell, 1979), ch. 8.

138. Cmnd. 3703, p. 11.

139. P. Hall, *Reforming the Welfare* (London: Heinemann, 1976), p. 16. 'Report of the Committee on Children and Young Persons' (Ingleby), Cmnd. 1191 (1960); Scottish Home and Health Department and Scottish Education Department, 'Children and Young Persons in Scotland' (Kilbrandon), Cmnd. 2306 (1964); *Crime a Challenge to Us All: Report of the Labour Party Study Group* (Longford) (1964).

140. Cooper, *Creation of the British Personal Social Services*, p. 65; and Hall, *Reforming the Welfare*, p. 28.

141. Department of Environment Archives, JS 3169 57 M62, file 71, Association of County Medical Officers of Health Evidence.

142. R.M. Titmuss, 'Social work and social science: a challenge for local government', *Royal Society of Health Journal*, 86 (1966), pp. 19–21.

143. Hall, *Reforming the Welfare*, pp. 34–5.

144. R.M. Titmuss, 'Care or cant', *Spectator*, 17 March 1961, pp. 354–5; and 'Community Care: Fact or Fiction?', address to Mental Health Conference (1961) in Titmuss Papers, LSE, file 135.

145. Titmuss Papers (Private), Titmuss to J.N. Morris, 19/6/67.

146. P.P., 'The Development of Community Care Plans for the Health and Welfare Services of Local Authorities in England and Wales', Cmnd. 1973, 1962–3, xxi, 265.

147. C. Ham, *Health Policy in Britain* (London: Macmillan, 1982), p. 21; and J. Allsopp, *Health Policy and the NHS* (London: Longmans, 1984), p. 57.

148. Titmuss Papers, LSE, file 122, I.G. Davies' paper on 'The Health and Welfare Plan', report by M.D. Warren (1963). This document summarises the substance of the discussion following the presentation of Davies' paper.

149. G.E. Rehin, H. Houghton, F.M. Martin, 'Mental health social work in hospitals and local authorities: a description of two work situations', in *Problems and Progress in Medical Care*, ed G.McLachlan (Oxford: Oxford University Press for the Nuffield Provincial Hospitals Trust,

1964), p. 324.
150. 'A realistic look at mental health services', editorial, *Medical Officer*, 111 (1964), p. 181.
151. CMO, C141, e.g. D.E. Cullington, MOH for Berkshire, to Ramage, 4/4/66.
152. SMOH, CI/111, Joint meeting, County and County Borough Group, 12/4/62.
153. Ministry of Health and Department of Health for Scotland, *Report of the Working Party on Social Workers in the Local Authority health and Welfare Services* (London: HMSO, 1959).
154. 'Social work in local authority health and welfare services', editorial, *Public Health*, 73 (1959), pp. 323–5; 'Social work in health and welfare', editorial, *Medical Officer*, 102 (1959), p. 274.
155. 'Social workers in the local authority health and welfare services', Special Report, *Public Health*, 73 (1959), p. 325.
156. Ministry of Health, Department of Home and Health for Scotland, Ministry of Education, *An Inquiry into Health Visiting*.
157. CMO, D160, C.D.L. Lycett, 'Social Workers and the Medical Officer of Health', 1964.
158. C.P. Blacker, *Problem Families: Five Inquiries* (London: Eugenics Society, 1952), p. 12.
159. S.W. Savage, 'Intelligence and infant mortality in problem families', *BMJ*, I (1964), p. 86; C.F. Brockington, *Problem Families,* Occasional Papers, No. 2, British Social Hygiene Council, 1949; R.C. Wofinden, *Problem Families in Bristol,* Occasional Papers in Eugenics, No. 6, (London: Eugenics Society and Cassell, 1960).
160. Women's Group on Public Welfare, *Our Towns* (Oxford: Oxford University Press, 1943).
161. Women's Group on Public Welfare, *The Neglected Child and His Family* (Oxford: Oxford University Press, 1948).
162. R.M. Titmuss, Foreword to A.F. Philp and N. Timms *The Problem of the Problem Family* (London: Family Service Units, 1962).
163. 'Medical and social welfare', editorial, *BMJ* 2 (1966), pp. 1216–17.
164. Titmuss Papers, LSE, file 96B, 'Doctors and the Social Services', typescript.
165. Ministry of Health, Central Health Service Council Standing Medical Advisory Committee, *The Field of Work of the Family Doctor* (London: HMSO, 1963).
166. R.M. Titmuss, 'The role of the family doctor today', p. 3.
167. Letter. R.W. Elliott, *Lancet*, I (1965), p. 212.
168. N. Deakin, 'Local government and social policy', in *Half a Century of Municipal Decline*, p. 207.

3 From public health to community medicine: the making of a new specialty 1968–1974

In the same year as the Seebohm Report threatened to remove the fastest growing and some of the most interesting responsibilities of the MOsH's work, the government also published its first Green Paper on the reorganization of the NHS. Where Seebohm threatened decimation, the Green Paper reassured MOsH that the importance of their work had not gone unrecognized, and that they would find a new, expanded (albeit unspecified) role as community physicians—specialists in community medicine—within the NHS.[1]

The British government was not alone in seeking the solution to spiralling health care costs in a more rational, integrated health care system, within which it was hoped that resources might be more easily shifted away from the expensive acute hospital sector. The evidence offered by T. McKeown[2] that acute medicine had in any case not made a major contribution to the improvement in health status during the nineteenth and early twentieth centuries, provided additional justification for such a strategy. By 1972 it was clear from government policy documents[3] that the new post of community physician was being viewed as a lynch-pin in the new integrated NHS structure.

However, the concept of the community physician and community medicine was developed in the first place by academics in the field of social medicine, who believed that the practice of public health had to be reformed if it were to survive. The efforts to reform the public health curriculum in the late 1950s and early 1960s emphasized epidemiology as the core element in public health education, with the intention that the public health doctor would become a broad advisor to the health service.[4] As R. Titmuss commented, the material collected by the Seebohm Committee seemed to provide more evidence as to the essential weakness of public health departments and their failure either to analyse or to deal effectively with the new health problems manifested in the changing patterns of mortality and morbidity. J.N. Morris, who sat on the Seebohm Committee and kept Titmuss informed of its findings, was the first person in the field of public health and social medicine formally to define the concept of the community physician in 1969,[5] and the Faculty of Community Medicine was established thereafter in 1972.

In giving shape to the specialty of community medicine via the new NHS structure, policy-makers significantly altered the concept of the community physician's role. Academics had stressed the importance of the community physician using specialist skills, primarily in epidemiology, to analyse health problems. Morris also hoped that such a role would allow the community physician to play a greater part in integrating the health services. In the government's policy documents issued prior to the reorganization of the NHS, the community physician's planning and management role within the integrated service was made the clear priority. As Morris commented, community medicine was born 'under forced circumstances, under pressure of events'.[6] In fact, it seems that the specialty was born largely of administrative fiat, with its identity and its future bound closely to that of the reorganized health service.

During a tour of the USA in the mid-1970s, Sir George Godber, the chief medical officer at the DHSS, was asked,

I am curious to know . . . how it was decided that someone who was already trained as a physician would definitely be needed for this position [of community physician], or was that not debated at all in the service? Was it just assumed that one could start with physicians and then add epidemiology and other skills to that?

Godber's reply was revealing: 'I think it was glanced at and not seriously considered.'[7] When the NHS was reorganized, a place had to be found for the displaced public health doctors and the relatively small group of medical administrators employed by the regional hospital boards (there were only fourteen senior administrative medical officers). Both groups were drawn into the specialty of community medicine, together with academics in the field. Thus the practitioners brought very different kinds of experiences to their new tasks, while the Faculty of Community Medicine (whose board was dominated by academics and government policy-makers) offered them rather different role prescriptions.

During the period between 1968 and the publication of the planning documents for the new NHS in 1972, MOsH reacted to proposals to create the post of community physician, struggling to translate them into practical realities, rather than taking the initiative themselves. Public health doctors accurately foresaw the problems inherent in the new NHS structure, in particular the possibility of tension between allegiance to their local communities and the NHS bureaucracy, and between the demands exerted by the hospital and by the community outside it, although these were issues over which they had little power in terms of policy-making. They were less successful in predicting the role of the new community physician. To the not altogether compatible expectations of academics and government, MOsH added ideas which tended to be based on their past experience rather than on an effort to reconceptualize their work.

In fact, while academics and policy-makers had clear conceptions of what they wanted community physicians to do, no one worked out how the community physician's role was to be made operational within the new structure. As a result, the role of the community physician was dictated in large part by the structure itself. This is turn helps to explain the tensions many community physicians have experienced in terms of both their role as specialist advisors and managers, and, as many MOsH foresaw, of their conflicting allegiances within the new structure, to their communities and to the NHS bureaucracy, and to the hospital and the community beyond it.

ACADEMICS DEFINE THE ROLE OF THE COMMUNITY PHYSICIAN

Academics in the field of public health, particularly those who were professors of social medicine, were convinced that public health had to be pushed in a new direction. The term 'community medicine' was something of a compromise; Titmuss, for example, favoured the concept but felt that community medicine was not as good a name as social and preventive medicine.[8]

J.N. Morris was one of the most influential critics of the work public health departments were doing. He believed strongly that public health practice should be grounded more firmly in the principles of modern epidemiology. His textbook on epidemiology identified the major uses of the subject as historical study, community diagnosis, analysis of the workings of health services, analysis of individual risks and chances, the identification of syndromes and the completion of the clinical picture.[9] From this he evolved the concept of a community physician responsible for community diagnosis and thus providing the 'intelligence' necessary for efficient and effective administration of the health service. The community physician would carry out the studies that would provide the basis for a discussion of rationing and other issues involving the 'morality of medical care'. The community physician's other major concern, according to Morris, would be the effective integration of the three parts of the NHS. Morris's main aim was to stress the complementarity of community medicine and clinical medicine, and to give public health a higher status within the medical profession, as well as a new role.

While he eschewed the attempt of some American epidemiologists to 'rescue' epidemiology from public health and bring it back to the 'laps of practising physicians',[10] Morris nevertheless approached prevention through the needs of the individual, believing that a multi-causal, epidemiological approach would ensure consideration of socio-economic and environmental variables and eliminate the danger of 'blaming the victim' for his illness. Using the example of coronary heart disease, he argued that the barriers between prevention and cure were crumbling and that 'public health needs clinical medicine—clinical medicine needs a community'.[11] By building his examples around specific non-infectious diseases, he emphasized the importance of co-operation with clinicians as one of the major aims of the new community medicine.

Morris's ideas were fed directly into two crucial policy documents of the late 1960s. The Todd Commission on medical education, which reported in 1968, was the first major government document to define community medicine.[12] One of the members of the Commission was Titmuss, who had, of course, worked with Morris since the late 1930s. The Todd Commission clearly articulated the two main strands of Morris's formulation of community medicine, when it defined it as the 'specialty practised by epidemiologists and administrators of medical services'.[13] It recommended closer links with clinical medicine and the introduction of vocational registration for community medicine specialists. (Informal discussions regarding the setting up of a Faculty of Community Medicine began in 1969.) The Commission commented on the 'unfortunate tendency for teachers and research workers in community medicine to pursue their interests separately from practitioners of the specialty'.[14] Like Morris, the Commission desired to impose greater academic rigour on the practice of public health, and in so doing to change its orientation. For the Todd Commission envisaged environmental health services and social work services leaving the public health department. Nor did its definition of community medicine encompass the work of the clinical medical officers, whose routine duties could not, in the eyes of the Commission, 'provide a doctor with an entirely satisfying career'.[15] Thus it was felt that 'the MOH in his traditional form, with both clinical and administrative functions, may well disappear completely, while the role of medical administrators was expected to grow in importance'.[16] The Commission intended to unite all doctors involved in medical administration, whether as employees of local government, the regional hospital boards, the Ministry of Health or industry, in the specialty of community medicine. Medical officers with regional hospital boards had already indicated their desire for a more specialized training.[17]

In 1968, the Seebohm Committee also reported on the future of the personal social services.[18] Morris was the only medically qualified member of the Committee. In a paragraph that, as the *Medical Officer* recognized,[19] bore all the hallmarks of Morris's thinking, it was stated that 'weakness' existed in the public health departments.[20] Furthermore, the 'widening character of prevention' demanded the joint effort of all the medical services.[21] The Report did not want the MOH to deploy social workers directly but rather to integrate the work of health service personnel and social service departments in providing for handicapped children, the chronic sick, the infirm aged and the mentally ill. It was argued that modern epidemiology should concentrate on providing the intelligence system necessary for their joint effort. The strong hint in the Report was that the MOH would perform the new tasks of community medicine better from a position more closely and administratively linked with clinical medicine. The Report had a clear notion of prevention as it related to social work, consisting of first an early intervention strategy, designed to fend off the emotional, intellectual, social and physical deprivation of the child, and second, general community-wide policies especially in housing and education 'aimed at creating an environment conducive to social well-being'.[22] The clear implication was that doctors had failed to grasp this concept of the social and that social workers must break free of medical control if they were to develop it. While effectively recommending the end of the local authority public health department, the Report nevertheless urged that there was important work for the MOH to do in the future and that it would be 'tragic' if his vital contribution were to be weakened even temporarily.

The publication of the first Green Paper on the reorganization of the NHS was planned to coincide with that of the Seebohm Report and was designed to reassure public health doctors. While clearly envisaging a diminution in the environmental health duties of the MOH, the Green Paper assured MOsH that with the concentration of their 'functions and powers' in the new organization would come 'the opportunity to develop their important role, and the skills of their staff'. The specifics of the community physician's task were not spelled out, although the idea that the community physician would be responsible for 'the epidemiological evaluation of the standards of health in each area'[23] was in tune with academic thinking at this point. Thus on the one hand MOsH were being threatened with extinction, while on the other they were being promised a larger role than ever before.

MOsH INTERPRET COMMUNITY MEDICINE AND THE ROLE OF THE COMMUNITY PHYSICIAN, 1968–1971

The reactions of the MOsH to the policy documents of 1968 were complex, reflecting the ambivalence they felt about their ties to local government, as opposed to a centrally-organized NHS, and to a community population outside the hospital as opposed to one that included the hospital. Their immediate reactions were, not surprisingly, often defensive. However, a number of leaders in the field looked forward more optimistically to the future and attempted to lay out in some detail what they felt the work of the community physician would entail. These attempts are noteworthy, not only for the wide variety of interpetations that are represented, but for the way in which they are grounded in those elements of past experience which the authors wished to see projected into the future. It was in all probability an impossible task to envisage the workings of the reorganized NHS and the role of the community physician within it. While some writers were able to spot some of the fundamental tensions the community physician would experience as a result of his place in the new structure, none was able to foresee their implications for his role and status.

In 1968 and 1969 the Society of Medical Officers of Health met to discuss both Seebohm and the first Green Paper on NHS reorganization. In 1964 Scottish MOsH had already protested the proposals of the Kilbrandon Committee for setting up a family social work service. They complained bitterly about the way in which advice was taken from social scientists like Titmuss:

It is most unfortunate that the advice of the academic advisors was not leavened with the practical experience of MOsH who are responsible for the administration and organization of the combined health and welfare services for 80 per cent of the population of Scotland.[24]

The Scottish MOsH claimed that local authority health and welfare departments were a 'going concern' despite shortages of professionally qualified staff. They were also angry that the Committee's Report did not acknowledge that health embraced social well-being.

The Society of Medical Officers of Health and the BMA were late in addressing the implications of the Seebohm proposals, especially in view of the advanced warning provided by the Scottish report. Above all the Seebohm Report aroused anger, which the paragraph introduced by Morris was not sufficient to quell. Both major interpretations of the 'Seebohm Revolution'[25] agree that medical opinion was not prepared for the Committee's recommendations, in part because the low status of public health meant that the BMA took little notice of the Committee until it was too late. Faced by what the *Medical Officer* described early in 1969 as the 'Seebohm now lobby . . . reminiscent of the "Second Front in 1942" campaign,';[26] medical opinion had swiftly to revise its approach. In so doing, the medical organizations did not all adopt the same strategy. The BMA modified its position during the course of the year to encompass some reform of social services, advocating the unification of child and welfare services in a single department. This enabled them to reach a compromise with the County Council's Association, which was in favour of combining most personal social services in one department, and which was additionally suspicious of the medical profession in respect to the tack it might take on NHS reorganization.[27] The Society of Medical Officers of Health, also seeing the writing on the wall, confined its official representations in 1969 to the argument that particular socio-medical services, especially for the mentally ill, should continue to be controlled by the MOH. However, the official position of the Association of County Medical Officers remained opposed to any reform and committed to the memo it presented in 1966 to the County Councils' Association:

The Association of County Medical Officers considers that where the need for social workers either for individuals or for the purposes of general community welfare, directly arises from and is related to a continuing medical cause, then responsibility for the main services required should vest in the Health Committee.[28]

Debate among the County Medical Officers of Health Group of the Society of Medical Officers of Health during 1968 and 1969 showed that the majority remained antagonistic to the Report and dismissed it as 'rubbish', insisting that social

work should remain medically controlled.[29] This body of
opinion doubted 'that there was an entity called social work'
and openly derided social workers' claims to professional
status.[30] These MOsH felt that the importance social workers
attached to casework was nothing more than mystique and
differed in no significant respect from the work done by health
visitors. Dr J.J.A. Reid, then county medical officer for
Buckinghamshire, made a strong attempt to moderate these
views, insisting that there was a discipline for social work as
much as for medicine.[31] The county medical officers stuck by
their justification of medical control of social workers by
arguing a medical cause for social problems. However, as M.
Jefferys effectively argued at the time, the boundary line
between health and welfare was next to impossible to draw.[32]
As one MOH also admitted, 'quite frankly even I do not know
when a case becomes one for the Welfare Department or is a
mental health problem'.[33] Dr R.C. Wofinden, MOH for
Bristol, was undoubtedly right to deplore the divorce between
the medical and social,[34] but the claim for medical control
could not be justified. Such a claim only served to justify
Seebohm's implicit charge that doctors had failed to
understand the social. MOsH had a strong case only in regard
to mental health social work, on which both the BMA and the
Society of Medical Officers of Health took a belated but strong
last-ditch stand in 1969.[35] But their efforts were to no avail, not
least because the Association of Psychiatric Social Workers,
who were well-qualified, supported the Seebohm proposals.

Morris believed that the Seebohm recommendations created
a structure that would allow social workers to collaborate with
education departments, health departments, housing and
supplementary benefit officials. When asked how community
physicians could be expected to practise good community
medicine when the Report threatened to remove the social
from their grasp, he replied that collaboration did not require
domination and that community physicians must learn to
work as members of interdisciplinary teams.[36] The problem
with the recommendations both for the future of the social
services and for the reorganization of the NHS was that,
although the elements of the structure were fully elaborated,
the functional linkages between them were not. In view of this,

the defence of medical domination of social services by those MOsH who believed that the NHS was likely to be unified outside the control of the local authorities and that the MOH therefore needed to maintain control over a team of workers[37] was not entirely unjustified. The fear of being 'left without troops' had been the immediate reaction of MOsH when first faced by the idea of integrating the medical services with the publication of the Porritt Report on medical services in 1962.[38] When many community physicians ended up working single-handed after 1974, this fear was realized.

However, an influential minority of MOsH looking more to the Green Paper on NHS reorganization than to Seebohm, agreed that social work should go its own way and were quite prepared to look ahead to the new role of the community physician. In 1968 Dr J.L. Gilloran, MOH for Edinburgh and the chairman of the Scottish Home and Health Department's Committee on Community Medicine, which reported in 1973, warned his colleagues south of the border that in Scotland the battle was over:

Our colleagues in England and Wales still have a choice. They can decide to imitate King Canute against the social work tide, or if they are realistic, accept Seebohm and direct their energies towards securing a prominent place for preventive medicine and MOsH in the recognised [*sic*] structure of the NHS now heralded by the Green Paper.

Gilloran urged brusquely that the social work profession had 'chosen its own bed of nails and should be allowed to lie on it';[39] the future of the MOH lay with community medicine not social work. As Dr J. Leiper, county MOH for Cumberland, reportedly observed in the course of the Society of Medical Officers of Health discussion:

The pearl of great price in this barrow was the community physician, the central point in the health centres, the man who was going to administer the thing, the middle of the see-saw, seeing that there was not too much spent on hospital work which was not associated with improvement in mortality statistics, the man who could edge the money away to be spent on an effective, efficient service. Medical Officers might have to pay for this by losing contact with the social services.[40]

MOsH were attracted to the idea of community medicine

and the position of the community physician chiefly because they understood that it meant a substantial rise in status for the specialty. After the publication of the Todd Commission's Report, J.H.F. Brotherston referred quite accurately to 'the time-bomb of specialist status'.[41] MOsH were also pleased with the Todd Commission's definition of community medicine, finding it to be satisfactorily wide and lacking only 'the inclusion of a reference to the importance of the organization of medical care and management'.[42] As the policy documents of the early 1970s moved closer to defining the community physician's planning and management role in the health service as central, so MOsH were better pleased. However, most MOsH were seeking recognition of their past work in administering services; at no time were they able to conceptualize the nature of their management role in the reorganized NHS.

In the discussions of their future place in the NHS, MOsH showed considerable awareness of the problems of coming under the control of central government and of forging working relationships with other doctors in the health service, particularly in the hospital sector. They had considerably more difficulty in coming up with a job description for the new community physicians. The first Green Paper did not close off the option of uniting the NHS under local government and on this, as on so much else, the opinion of MOsH was divided. Many were not convinced that local authority control was advisable. Of the two major papers on the Seebohm Report and the Green Paper presented to the Association of County Medical Officers, the one by G.W. Knight and J.J.A. Reid, expressing greater ambivalence about local authority control, received a more enthusiastic response. As it remarked, 'the past history of local government involvement in health services is not entirely satisfactory'.[43] Another MOH wrote more strongly still to Dr G. Ramage, secretary of the Association, urging that local authorities should not 'be entrusted with the management of a comprehensive health service', citing the vexed politics of fluoridization in support of his argument.[44] Certainly many MOsH were anxious to escape both local politics and the continuous struggles with local authorities over pay.

On the other hand several letters to the editor of the *Medical Officer* in 1968 expressed outrage at the possible end to the MOH's relationship with local government.[45] Other correspondents also expressed anxiety over the allied issue of accountability. The MOH's public accountability to a body elected by the population he served was felt to be a crucial part of his watchdog role as guardian of the people's health, and the personal relationship with his community was perceived as an important source of information and control.[46] The secretary of the Association of Municipal Corporations also raised the issue of finance and the fear that the demands of public health would be subordinated to those of the hospital system within a unified NHS.[47]

Both these issues were destined to become important after 1974. But MOsH had little influence over the basic decisions as to the final shape of NHS reorganization. In 1969 a deputation from the BMA's Public Health Committee asked the minister, Crossman, to wait for the Royal Commission on Local Government to report before making a final decision on the possibility of unification under the local authorities, but Crossman refused, having decided that it would not be possible to finance the NHS via local government.[48] In many respects the poor morale of the public health service was reflected in the poor image of local government during the late 1960s, the main problems of the latter being the relationship between size and function, and perceived conflict between local democracy and efficiency.[49]

While some leading MOsH continued to hope for integration of the NHS under the local authorities throughout 1969, others anticipated correctly that the NHS would be unified outside and the social services inside local government. They therefore began to press for the appointment of community physicians at all levels in the new structure (something that was not secured until the release of the policy documents of 1972) and 'coterminosity' between the boundaries of the new NHS authorities and local government.[50] MOsH were assuming that much of their work would continue to revolve around the running of services, rather than thinking about the nature of their responsibilities within the organized NHS. They were well pleased when 'coterminosity' between the area health authorities (the middle tier of the new structure) and local authorities was guaranteed by the second Green Paper in 1970. They also expressed satisfaction by the apparent 'elevation' of the community physician to the area tier, while continuing to ask that community physicians be appointed at all levels of the new structure.[51] In fact, the area tier was not central to the workings of the other health services, especially the hospitals. After 1974 many of the leading MOsH who became area medical officers found to their chagrin that the districts were more crucial to the planning process; indeed in the further reorganization of the NHS in 1982 the areas disappeared.

Closely linked to the issue of local versus central government control was the relationship of public health to the other parts of the health service, especially to the hospital sector. Those who were most anxious to preserve the MOH's connection with the local authorities were also more worried about possible domination of public health by the hospitals. On the other hand others looked forward to greater contact with the hospital, 'the fountainhead', as one put it.[52] The Bonham Carter Report on District General Hospitals, published in 1969, had suggested that the community physician might be based in the district general hospital,[53] and this was taken up with enthusiasm by some commentators, who felt that without close links to the hospital the development of fully integrated community health services would prove impossible.[54] Those expressing positive feelings about the relationship with the hospital stressed that in future the hospital would be considered a part of the community and not separate from it. As Sir George Godber put it, 'One must not think in terms of a general hospital that needed a district, but of a district that needed a general hospital.'[55] In their influential paper given to the Association of County Medical Officers, Knight and Reid made explicit reference to the Todd Report's description of the hospital as part of the community:

It is important to stress this as the suggested title 'community physician' might be taken to imply that his concern was solely with the segment of the health service lying outside the hospital. Perhaps it should be mentioned here that it is assumed that existing public health staff would be absorbed into the new structure and that, whilst some might be employed as community physicians, others would work with appropriate hospital departments.[56]

The academic case for community medicine stressed that the relationship between the new specialty and clinical medicine was complementary, and it was therefore a logical next step to press for stronger links with the hospital. In 1971 Brotherston argued that the MOH had become a mere auxiliary; the new prevention demanded a closer association with clinical medicine. He therefore argued the case for both MOsH and GPs re-establishing links with the hospital: 'The hospital is so central, so powerful, so educational within the modern health care system.'[57]

In the end the nature of the link between community medicine and the hospitals—indeed, the meaning of the community—depended in large part on the attitude of clinicians, and here, as with the final form of the reorganized NHS, MOsH could do little to influence the situation. After 1974 it became clear that few clinicians understood or accepted the idea that the community physician was in a position to look at all parts of the NHS. Indeed, even the third 'Cogwheel' Report from the committee charged with improving efficiency of medical work in the hospitals (published in 1974) clearly categorized community physicians with GPs, domiciliary nurses and social workers and those 'people providing services outside the hospital'.[58]

If MOsH were able to pinpoint the central difficulties inherent in trying to integrate public health doctors into the NHS, they were less successful in assessing the role of the community physician. On the whole, the tendency was to stress the elements of continuity rather than change. The idea expressed in the first Green Paper, that the job of the community physician represented an extension of the MOH's work rather than any radical departure was obviously reassuring. Knight and Reid observed in their paper:

The role will have to be spelt out in considerable detail and it would appear that, from his suggested use of epidemiology and other methods to measure the need for various forms of services and to assess the efficacy of these services, the community physician would in fact be continuing to carry out the function of a medical administrator, although working on a larger and more effective scale than at present.[59]

While MOsH made every effort to join the debate about the

future work of the community physician and to bring the possibilities to the notice of their colleagues through the Society of Medical Officers of Health and the medical journals, what is noteworthy is the way their various predictions reflected their own predilections and experience rather than a calculated assessment of what would be feasible in the new structure. A majority emphasized the importance of administration and management, reflecting the way in which the pre-1974 role of the MOH was taken up so much with planning and running services.

The early attempts to flesh out the community physician's future role which followed the 1968 policy document were often vague. A paper prepared for the BMA in 1969 by Dr C.D.L. Lycett, county MOH for Wiltshire, listed the tasks of the community physician at district level in terms that were familiar: assessing health needs and the workings of services, advising clinicians and local authorities, organizing the work of health visitors and taking responsibility for child and environmental health.[60] The description of the area medical officer's job as 'epidemiology in the wide sense' was much vaguer, the main point being only to insist that a community physician must also be appointed at area level. The second Green Paper broadly repeated this delineation of tasks for the community physician but ascribed them to the area medical officer.[61] Subsequent commentaries followed suit and proved as vague in their description of the district community physician's task as Lycett had been in respect to the area medical officer. The *Medical Officer* described the community physician at district level as the area community physician's 'local representative'.[62] A discussion reported in *Public Health* in 1969 also stressed that the duties of the MOH would continue to be important and emphasized the community physician's task of co-ordination at all levels of the medical organization, and of liaison with para-medical services, social services and local authorities.[63]

The Todd Commission had identified two broad components in its definition of community medicine, epidemiology and administration, and these were constantly referred to in the early papers on the community physician's role, but most commentators gave considerably more space to the administrative component. W. Parry wrote in 1970 of the importance of epidemiology particularly at district level, but little amplification of this role was ever offered.[64] R.W. Elliott's influential paper written in 1970 started from the position spelled out by J.N. Morris, that the barriers between prevention and cure were crumbling, and that the community physician would play an 'intimate coordinating role in the health service of the future'.[65] As well as listing the MOH's current tasks as part of the work of the future, Elliott paid considerable attention to what community physicians would be able to do for clinicians in terms of 'bridging the gaps' between clinical services. The *Medical Officer* also welcomed the role of the community physician as that of a 'genuine bridge', something promised when the NHS was established in 1948, but never fulfilled.[66]

In a paper published in the *Lancet* in 1970, Gooding, Yule and Reid, all medical officers in the Buckinghamshire County Health and Welfare Department, emphasized the 'synoptic view' the community physician would be able to bring to the NHS and the importance of planning for both the hospital and the community outside it.[67] In taking this view, they were building on the experience of the Buckinghamshire Department in planning the health care services for the new town of Milton Keynes. Implicit in their assumptions was the idea that the community physician would be able to call on a large staff. In a paper published in the same year, another MOH also assumed that there would be departments of community medicine, employing many different kinds of community physicians, including specialists in paediatrics, health education and epidemiology.[68] Similarly the Society of Medical Officers of Health's evidence to the Hunter Committee on Medical Administrators, submitted in 1970, mentioned departments of community medicine and assumed that staff would be forthcoming.[69] However, no specific provision was ever made for this in the English reorganization documents. Indeed, the Report on Management Arrangements for the reorganized NHS was to make clear in 1972 that at district level the community physician would be working on his own.[70] The Scottish documents were rather different in this respect. The Gilloran Report, published in 1973, made it clear that it envisaged the appointment of more community physicians than did the English policy documents, and it clearly stated the need to establish departments of community medicine, fully staffed by 'appropriate ancillary staff'.[71]

Gooding, Yule and Reid concluded that to make his planning role effective, the community physician 'should have not merely advisory functions but managerial ones also'.[72] This emphasis was the one adopted in the crucial policy documents published in 1972, which went a step further in envisaging the community physician's work as a means to effective planning and management of health *services*, rather than to a broader analysis of health *problems*.

FINALIZING THE ROLE OF THE COMMUNITY PHYSICIAN, 1970–1974: THE MEANING OF MEDICAL ADMINISTRATION

The Hunter Report on medical administrators was the first document to spell out the position of the community physician in the new NHS structure. It concentrated on explaining how community medicine was to fit into an integrated health service rather than on the aims and objectives of the new specialty. The community physician was seen as the key to effective integration of the health services, linking lay administrators to clinicians and co-ordinating the work of the NHS with that of the local authorities.[73] The main preoccupation of the Hunter Committee was how to make the new consensus management structure of the NHS work. Doctors had to be persuaded to become actively involved in the management of the health service, and it was in this context that the role of the community physician as a 'linkman', inspiring the confidence of both clinicians and administrators, was perceived as crucial.[74] The community physician was recognized as a specialist advisor, with particular skills in epidemiology, but, like Gooding, Yule and Reid, the Committee felt that he had to be more than advisor if his expertise was to be properly utilized. Thus while it was envisaged that a number of community physicians would act primarily as advisors, it was also clearly stated that 'a substantial number of doctors at all levels' would be involved in administrative work with management responsibilities.[75] The Hunter Report outlined the same tasks for the community physician at area level as the second Green Paper, with the crucial addition of 'planning' and 'management'. Again, the role of the district community physician was not spelled out.

The Report talked of epidemiology only as a means to assessing health needs, which were narrowly defined in terms of service provision.[76] No mention was made of prevention other than as it related to personal health services. The Report on Management Arrangements for the Reorganized NHS, also published in 1972, shared the Hunter Committee's preoccupation with making the new consensus management structure work. The specialist in community medicine was described as being 'involved full-time in the planning and organization of health services and in the provision of general preventive, screening and clinic services'.[77] Like the Hunter Committee, the Management Report insisted that the community physician should be more than an advisor and should take his place on the formal management teams of the NHS. The Report defined three roles for the community physician, as specialist, advisor and manager.[78] All three were closely geared to ensuring the effective operation of the reorganized NHS. As a specialist the community physician would stimulate integration and link the various parts of the service (no mention was made of epidemiological skills); as advisor he would liaise with the local authorities; and as a manager he would be responsible for planning, information, evaluation of service effectiveness and the co-ordination of preventive care services. The roles of specialist/advisor and manager formed the core of subsequent definitions of the community physician's role, including that of the Faculty of Community Medicine.[79] But debate has centred on whether these roles are of equal importance. There seems no doubt but that in the policy documents of 1972 the role of the community physician was envisaged primarily as a means of integrating the NHS and of achieving effective consensus management.

The Consultative Document on reorganization, also issued by the government in 1972, stated that:

Their [the community physicians'] concern will be with assessing need for health services, evaluating the effectiveness of existing services and planning the best use of health resources. Equally, they will concern themselves with developing preventive health services, with the links between the health and the local authority personal social, public health and education services, and with providing the medical advice and help which local authorities will need for the administration of those and other services.[80]

This apparently attached equal importance to the community physician's role of manager and of specialist advisor. However, the latter was again narrowly confined to service provision, and the whole passage was placed in the section entitled 'A Sound Management Structure'. This final government document on reorganization made effective management throughout the NHS a priority, and it is therefore not unreasonable to suggest that particular importance was attached to the community physician's planning and management role.

After the publication of the policy documents in 1972, practitioners expressed some concern that the community physician's role was in danger of being too narrowly defined. Dr G. Ramage, the secretary of the Association of County Medical Officers of Health, was typical in wholeheartedly welcoming the boost the Hunter Report gave to medical administration, but in also questioning exactly what was meant by 'administration' and what would be the fate of prevention, public health's traditional task:

The Working Party's whole report is directed to medical administration .... I do not know how the Working Party regards 'medical administration', but I see a great need to preserve the preventive outlook and would like any refresher course to deal with the place of prevention in all parts of the new services.[81]

MOsH were happy with the idea that they should administer and co-ordinate services, but few grasped the full implications of the consensus management structure. As one commented, the concept of management was too vague, and he was not clear as to whether it involved 'monitoring' or 'co-ordination', nor was he clear as to where power and authority lay.[82] Confusion as to the meaning of management and administration persisted after 1974. Used to a hierarchical structure, the MOH had no experience of a consensus management approach. Furthermore, he would join the new management teams with few staff and, despite specialist status, in a weak position professionally.

The BMA also viewed the definition of community medicine primarily in terms of 'administration' with some suspicion, fearing that it would weaken community medicine's claim to specialist skills. In its evidence to the Hunter Committee, the BMA's Public Health Committee stated that it wished 'to stress at once that it regards community medicine primarily as a discipline covering the whole health of the community as a community, and not necessarily anchored to administrative considerations'.[83]

There were few attempts to tackle Ramage's other concern about the future of prevention. Morris had written of the importance of prevention at the individual level, taking coronary heart disease as an example.[84] The same example was pursued by the Hunter Committee, but in terms of the contribution that the community physician would be able to make to the clinical processes of examination, diagnosis and decision.[85] In 1971 Dr A. Gatherer attempted to spell out the implications of the kind of shifts identified by Morris for preventive medicine, redefining primary prevention as health promotion and pointing to the role of the GP in secondary and tertiary prevention.[86] Gatherer was almost alone at this time in also stressing the importance of an ecological approach to prevention and of a broader consideration of environmental issues as part of the community physician's task. Most MOsH were concerned that their responsibility for communicable disease control and personal preventive services should continue, but they did not attempt to redefine community medicine's preventive goals more broadly. Even the commitment to traditional preventive services was tempered for some by reluctance to support the cause of the clinical medical officers, described by one MOH as 'pin-money women', who were not worthy of specialist status.[87] Most clinical medical officers failed to achieve membership of the Faculty of Community Medicine in 1974.

Thus MOsH moved into the role of community physician believing that they were to be the lynch-pin of the new NHS, co-ordinating and administering services, but they had little idea as to the meaning of their formal role in the new management structure or of the place of 'management' in their total package of tasks and concerns. They correctly perceived the possibility of tension between allegiance to their committee and their formal accountability to the NHS bureaucracy, and between the demands of the hospital and of the 'community' beyond it. But what is most striking is the lack of attention they paid to the way in which their roles would be made operational in the new structure and to the formulation of goals for the new specialty. In respect to the latter, the absence of discussion on the future of prevention is particularly noteworthy. It is hard to avoid the conclusion that MOsH believed that the new post of community physician would mean little more than welcome expansion of their old tasks and powers. In reality, the structural constraints of their new position tended to dictate their role.

The Faculty of Community Medicine, while adopting the Committee on Management Arrangements' definition of the community physician as specialist, advisor and manager, tended in its training to stress epidemiology as the skill base, arguing that management is about change which is achieved only by presenting a case based on careful research. Since its establishment in 1972, the Faculty has been happy to encourage greater links with clinical medicine and to stress, in the manner of Morris, the complementarity between community medicine and clinical medicine. This concept of community medicine has differed from that of government, which clearly believed that the main task of community physicians was to recommend changes in the deployment of resources and to convince their clinical colleagues of their necessity. In the view of the Faculty, the community physician advises and stands back, but it was the hope of the policy documents of 1972 that he would play a leading part in securing the acquiescence of his colleagues to change. In Gill's view the role of community physicians could 'be interpreted as an additional mechanism for increasing the accountability of the profession through internal review and evaluation'.[88]

NOTES

1. Ministry of Health, *National Health Service: The Administrative Structure f the Medical and Related Services in England and Wales* (London: HMSO, 1968).
2. T. McKeown, *The Modern Rise of Population* (London: Edward Arnold, 1976).
3. DHSS, *Report of the Working Party on Medical Administrators* (London: HMSO, 1972); and *Report of the Working Party on Management Arrangements for the Reorganized NHS* (London: HMSO, 1972).
4. See above, p. 79.
5. See, in particular, J.N. Morris, 'Tomorrow's community physician', *Lancet*, II (1969), pp. 811–16.
6. J.N. Morris, 'The Specialty of Community Medicine', paper given at a conference on 'Administrative Medicine and the Health Services of the Future', University of Aberdeen, 25 September 1968, tape held by the Wellcome Institute for the History of Medicine, CMAC Acc. No. 6.
7. DHEW, *The British Health Service: Conversations with Sir George Godber* (Washington, D.C.: DHEW, 1976), p. 101.
8. T. Titmuss to J.A.D. Anderson, London School of Hygiene and Tropical Medicine, 8/5/67, Titmuss Papers (Private). H. Francis has traced the origin of the term 'community physician' in his 'Towards community medicine: the British experience', in *Recent Advances in Community Medicine*, ed A.E. Bennett (Edinburgh: Livingstone, 1978), p. 9.
9. J.N. Morris, *The Uses of Epidemiology* (Edinburgh: Livingstone, 1969; first pub. 1957).
10. J.N. Paul, *Clinical Epidemiology* (Chicago: University of Chicago Press, 1958), p. 40, quoted in D. Roth, 'The scientific basis of epidemiology: an historical and philosophical enquiry', unpub. Ph.D. thesis, University of California and Berkeley, 1976, p. 16.
11. Morris, 'Tomorrow's community physician', p. 814.
12. P.P., 'Report of the Royal Commission on Medical Education', Cmnd. 3569, 1967–8, xxv, p. 569, para. 133.
13. *ibid.*
14. *ibid.*, para. 144.
15. *ibid.*, para. 147.
16. *ibid.*, para. 51. ,
17. 'Report on the Training of Doctors for the Administration of Hospitals and Public Health Services', in *Vocational Training in Medicine: Reports of Three Working Parties* (Oxford: Nuffield Provincial Hospitals Trust, 1967), pp. 39–55.
18. P.P., 'Report of the Committee on Local Authority and Allied Personal Social Services', Cmnd. 3703, 1967–8, xxxii, p. 157.
19. 'Exit the MOH: enter the community physician', editorial, *Medical Officer*, 120 (1968), p. 69.
20. Cmnd. 3703, para. 385.

21. *ibid.*

22. *ibid.*, para. 434.

23. Ministry of Health, *The Administrative Structure of the Medical and Related Services*, pp. 47 and 32.

24. BMA Archives, Joint Committee of the BMA and the Society of Medical Officers of Health on Social Work and the Community, 1966–7, Item 780, Memo of the Scottish Society of Medical Officers of Health to the Scottish Home and Health Department, n.d.

25. P. Hall, *Reforming the Welfare: The Politics of Change in the Personal Social Services* (London: Heinemann, 1976); and J. Cooper, *The Creation of the British Personal Social Services* (London: Heinemann, 1983).

26. 'Hastening slowly', editorial, *Medical Officer*, 121 (1969), p. 61.

27. Hall, *Reforming the Welfare*, p. 99.

28. Records of the County Medical Officers of Health held by the Wellcome Institute for the History of Medicine (hereafter CMO), C141, Association of County Medical Officers, Memo to the County Councils' Association, 20/4/66.

29. CMO, A28, Discussion on the Seebohm Committee, Report and the Green Paper, 20/9/68, p. 18.

30. *ibid.*, p. 11; also CMO, D160, 'Social Workers and the MOH', paper by C.D.L. Lycett, 17/11/64.

31. CMO, A28, Discussion on the Seebohm Committee, Report and the Green Paper, 20/9/68, p. 11.

32. M. Jefferys, 'The boundaries of community medicine: with the social work services', *Public Health*, 84 (1969), pp. 29–38.

33. CMO, C141, Dr G. Nisbet to E.P. Smith, clerk of the County Council of Huntingdon, 17/3/66.

34. R.C. Wofinden, 'Strategy and tactics for the public health service', *Public Health*, 83 (1969), pp. 89–96.

35. Hall, *Reforming the Welfare*, pp. 99–102.

36. Morris, 'The specialty of community medicine'.

37. BMA, Public Health Committee, 1968–9, Item 667, Doc. 6, Comments of C.D.L. Lycett on the Report of the Committee on Local Authority and Allied Personal Social Services, 31/7/68.

38. 'The crux for public health', *Medical Officer*, 109 (1963), p. 291.

39. J.L. Gilloran, letter, *Medical Officer*, 120 (1968), pp. 238–9.

40. CMO, A28, Discussion on the Seebohm Committee Report and the Green Paper, 20/9/68, p. 26.

41. J.H.F. Brotherston, 'The future of the public health doctor', *Public Health*, 84 (1970), p. 58.

42. BMA, Public Health Committee, 1968–9, Item 667, Doc. 16, 'Memo of the Joint Working Party of the Public Health Committee and the Society of Medical Officers of Health on the Report of the Royal Commission on Medical Education'.

43. CMO, C113, Comments by G.W. Knight and J.J.A. Reid on the Green Paper, January 1969.

44. *ibid.*, A. Elliott to G. Ramage, 17/12/68.

45. E.g. J. Galloway's letter, *Medical Officer*, 120 (1968), p. 127.
46. CMO, A28, Discussion on the Seebohm Committee Report and the Green Paper, 20/9/68, p. 3.
47. J.C. Swaffield, 'The medical officer of health in local government', *Public Health*, 83 (1969), pp. 293–8.
48. BMA, Public Health Committee, 1968–9, Item 667, Doc. 41, 'Administrative Structure of the NHS in England and Wales', Deputation to Crossman, 5/3/69.
49. C. Pearce, *The Machinery of Change in Local Government, 1888–1974* (London: Allen & Unwin, 1980), p. 110.
50. Comment of J.F. Warin, debate on Swaffield, 'The medical officer of health in local government', *Public Health*, 83 (1969), p. 298.
51. CMO, 135, Comments of the Society of Medical Officers of Health on the Second Green Paper, March 1970.
52. CMO, A28, Discussion on the Seebohm Committee Report and the Green Paper, 20/9/68, p. 26.
53. DHSS Welsh Office, Central Health Services Council, *Report of the Committee on the Functions of the District General Hospital* (London: HMSO, 1969), para. 466.
54. BMA, Public Health Committee, 1969–70, Item 686, Doc. 18, 'Population Groups for the Practice of Preventive Medicine', by W. Ferguson, p. 3; and W.H. Parry, 'The Community Physician of the Future', RSH Paper, November 1970, p. 2.
55. CMO, A30, Discussion of the Second Green Paper and the Authority Social Services Bill, 10/4/70, p. 9.
56. CMO, C113, Knight and Reid 'Comments', January 1969.
57. J.H.F. Brotherston, 'Change and the NHS', in *Management and the Health Services*, ed A. Gatherer and M.D. Warren (Oxford: Pergamon, 1971), p. 19.
58. DHSS, *Third Report of the Joint Working Party on the Organisation of Medical Work in Hospitals* (London: HMSO, 1974), para. 35.
59. CMO, C113, Knight and Reid 'Comments'.
60. BMA, Public Health Committee, 1968–9, Item 667, Doc. 35, 'The Future of Public Health and the Role of the Community Physician' by C.D.L. Lycett.
61. DHSS, *The Future Structure of the NHS* (London: HMSO, 1970).
62. 'The Crossman model', editorial, *Medical Officer*, 123 (1970), p. 91.
63. 'The future of the public health doctor', *Public Health*, 84 (1969), pp. 57–91.
64. Parry, 'The Community Physician of the Future', p. 2.
65. R.W. Elliott, *The Community Physician* (County Councils' Association, 1970), p. 2.
66. 'The Crossman model'.
67. D.G. Gooding, J.J.A. Reid, and I.G. Yule, 'The community physician's work', *Lancet*, I (1970), p. 712.
68. A. MacGregor, 'The community physician', *Medical Officer*, 123 (1970), pp. 95–6.
69. 'Evidence to the Hunter Working Party', editorial, *Medical Officer*, 125

(1971), p. 47.
70. DHSS, *Report of the Working Party on Medical Administrators*; and *Report of the Working Party on Management Arrangements for the Reorganized NHS*.
71. Scottish Home and Health Department, *Community Medicine in Scotland* (London: HMSO, 1973).
72. Gooding, Reid and Yule, 'The community physician's work', p. 714.
73. DHSS, *Report of the Working Party on Medical Administrators*, para. 18.
74. *ibid.*, para. 21.
75. *ibid.*, para. 5.
76. *ibid.*, para. 136.
77. DHSS, *Management Arrangements for the Reorganized NHS*, para. 4.1(b).
78. *ibid.*, paras 4.21, 4.22, 4.23.
79. Faculty of Community Medicine, 'Community medicine in the restructured NHS', *Community Medicine*, 1 (1981), pp. 236–42.
80. P.P., 'NHS Reorganisation: England', Cmnd, 5055 (London: HMSO, 1972), para. 142.
81. CMO, D130, Ramage to A.C. Hetherington, secretary, County Councils' Association, 19/5/71.
82. CMO, D131, 'Notes for Introducing a Discussion on NHS Reorganisation: England', by Dr A. Elliott, 5/9/72.
83. BMA, Public Health Committee, 1970–1, Item 705, Doc. 25, 'Evidence for the Hunter Working Party'.
84. See above, p. 103.
85. DHSS, *Report of the Working Party on Medical Administrators*, para. 22.
86. A. Gatherer, 'Community medicine: quo vadis?', in *Challenges for Change*, ed G. McLachlan (Oxford: Nuffield Provincial Hospitals Trust, 1971), pp. 95–128.
87. CMO, A30, Discussion of the Second Green Paper and the Local Authority Social Services Bill, 10/4/70, p. 18.
88. D. Gill, 'The reorganization of the National Health Service: some sociological aspects with special reference to the role of the community physician', in *The Sociology of the NHS*, ed M. Stacey, Sociological Review Monograph, No. 22 (Keele: University of Keele, 1976), p. 20.

4 A decade of community medicine 1974–1984

Posts for community physicians were created at region, area and district in the 1974 reorganization of the NHS. Regional medical officers, area medical officers and district community physicians carried formal management responsibilities in the new consensus management teams, while priority in appointing specialists in community medicine (equal in status to community physicians with management responsibilities) was given to those who would advise the local authorities on environmental health, child health and the social services.[1]

In his account of the reorganization of the NHS in Humberside, R.G.S. Brown commented that MOsH were among the best informed and most committed to the impending changes.[2] Yet by 1976 community physicians were asking publicly whether there was any future for community medicine.[3] The reasons for the disillusionment that followed so swiftly on the heels of reorganization were complex. In the first place, the transition for many, especially the more senior public health doctors, who comprised the vast majority of the new community physicians, was far from easy; secondly, the NHS was almost immediately beset by a severe financial crisis, and community physicians found themselves at the centre of conflicts over financial cutbacks; thirdly, community physicians were neither understood nor respected by their clinical colleagues, for, as Gill has pointed out, the community physician inherited the low status of the public health doctor;[4] and fourthly, community physicians experienced considerable difficulty in defining both their tasks and the aims of the new specialty.

There remained a substantial gap between academics and practitioners in the field of community medicine. The Faculty of Community Medicine continued to emphasize that the scientific basis of community medicine was epidemiology and that community physicians were specialists who applied epidemiological knowledge to health problems and health services. However, in practice, as D. Towell pointed out in 1977, this translated into an extremely complex role of manager, planner and specialist with a particular interest in prevention and environmental health.[5] A mere six years after the first community physicians were appointed, another restructuring of the NHS was proposed and with it a change in the nature and distribution of community physician posts. In 1982 the area tier was abolished and community physicians with management responsibilities at district were renamed district medical officers (DMOs). Community physicians remained uncertain as to what their priority concern should be or how far their work should be determined by the needs of the NHS.

The fortunes of community medicine were to a large extent bound up with the success or failure of the new NHS structure. While community physicians struggled to forge a role within it, both clinicians and government policy-makers tended to regard them as part and parcel of the new management structure. Clinicians suspected that community physicians were indeed intended to perform the monitoring role suggested by Gill, a suspicion that was fed by the part community physicians had to play in rationing resources as a result of the financial difficulties that began in the mid-1970s.[6] The government planning documents of 1972 had clearly envisaged the community physicians as the engine of integration, playing a crucial mediating role between administrators and clinicians. However, by 1980, the focus of concern had shifted from achieving effective integration and a redistribution of resources among the acute hospital services to clamping down on the seemingly endless upward spiral of hospital costs. This resulted in a parallel shift of emphasis from consensus management, originally viewed as a means to achieving integration, to a more straightforward and narrow concept of management as careful administration, with the articulation of clear lines of accountability.[7] Thus in the 1980s and most specifically since the publication of the Griffiths Report in

1984, the management role of the community physician has been eroded and with it the importance of the community physician in the eyes of government.

The analysis that follows draws on the same range of published and archival documents as the previous chapters, but is supplemented by material from semi-structured interviews with forty-three practising community physicians, representing all English health regions, all but three of whom made the transition to community medicine in 1974, and six academic founders of the specialty.*

THE TRANSITION TO COMMUNITY MEDICINE, 1974–1980

The human factor

As Brown commented in his study of reorganization in Humberside, the structural reform of 1974 was but a means to altering the 'appreciative self' of large numbers of people engaged in health service management.[8] There is little doubt but that the policy-makers of the early 1970s underestimated the difficulties in changing the attitudes, values and culture of those employed by the NHS. Medical officers of health were used to the hierarchical structure of local authorities and to dealing primarily with the administration of environmental health services. The reorganization of 1974 plunged them into, first, a specialty where all community physicians enjoyed equal status; second, consensus rather than line management; and third, the problems of the hospitals as well as the services outside them. It was unrealistic to expect them to begin to operate effectively overnight.

MOsH made a major contribution to planning for the reorganization at the same time that some local authorities were making substantial changes, introducing concepts such as corporate planning and programme budgeting.[9] However, most MOsH received only the bare minimum of retraining

*The forty-three community physicians included twenty-five district medical officers (DMOs) and eighteen specialists in community medicine (SCMs); fourteen of the latter were employed at district and four at region. Twelve of the forty-three were women and all but four of these were SCMs.

courses by way of preparation for 1974. Short Hunter courses for doctors were set up after the publication in 1972 of the Report on medical administrators. At the same time a Centre for Extension Training was set up at the London School of Hygiene and funded for five years by the DHSS. Many of the people I interviewed reported sitting through the courses in fear, anger and impatience. One felt that as a senior manager he had nothing to learn from academics who had never held such a position. Another recalled that when attending one of the courses he was suffering acute anxiety about his job prospects and felt that it showed a certain insensitivity on the part of his instructors when they chose to apply community medicine concepts to methods of coronary care. MOsH had a better chance of coming to terms with reorganization if they had either received more extensive preparation for 1974 in the form of a management course, or if they had obtained their DPH qualification in the late 1960s or early 1970s, when most courses were changing in content in response to the determination of many academics in the field to broaden the scope of medical administration.

There were no readily identifiable jobs for the 1974 entrants to apply for. In general, senior MOsH found themselves in competition with senior administrative medical officers from the hospital boards for the position of regional medical officer (RMO), which in the vast majority of cases was filled by the latter. MOsH of large county councils most commonly became area medical officers (AMOs). MOsH for small districts tended to compete for the post of district community physician (DCP) or specialist in community medicine (SCM) against second-line officers from the hospital boards and deputy MOsH from larger areas. Inevitably there were tensions. As one of my respondents explained, an MOH from a county borough might not wish to take a job as a DCP in an area where the MOH from the county council had become the AMO. Many senior clinical medical officers from public health departments also made the transition to community medicine, filling with few exceptions the positions of SCM (Child Health) or SCM (Social Services). Those doctors who, with an eye to the new mix of tasks that would be demanded of the community physician obtained experience in both the hospital board and public health sectors, tended to rise rapidly to the rank of RMO.

The search for a suitable post was often a harrowing one for public health doctors. They were allowed to apply for up to five posts at regional and five at area level.[10] The membership and procedures for selection committees were laid out carefully;[11] nevertheless candidates often faced a huge interviewing board and were told to speak only to certain members of it, the rest being there to interview for other posts. MOsH who had been strong-minded and determined had good reason to fear the opposition of local authority members of the selection committees. Finally public health doctors had reason to be concerned about the secrecy surrounding 'the matching process', by which the candidate listed his/her first choice of employment, the hiring committee did likewise, and at some point the lists were compared.[12]

The happiest people in 1974 were those relatively few senior medical officers who found that overnight they had achieved a considerable rise in salary, consultant status and liberation from the hierarchical structure of the public health department. One of my respondents who had joined a county borough public health department that was considered progressive, nevertheless described the work relationships as 'Dickensian' and would have left public health had it not been for the 1974 reorganization. The few clinical medical officers who became community physicians experienced the additional advantage that very little change in the content of their work was expected. They occupied the labelled posts of SCM (Social Services) and SCM (Child Health), which were filled first to reassure local authorities of continued assistance in running services. After reorganization, SCMs were permitted to supervise the work of clinical medical officers, who continued to run child, family planning and geriatric clinics, but not to engage in clinical practice.

The least happy groups in 1974 were those who failed to achieve membership of the Faculty of Community Medicine. Some 400 MOsH for small districts did not achieve specialist status and became latched-on officers. In the case of one SCM I interviewed, his supervisor in the public health department failed to gain Faculty membership and for the next eight years the two worked in reverse relationship. In another case, a latched-on officer continued to do the environmental health work in the district but final responsibility had to rest with the SCM. From the 1972 planning documents it had been clear that the clinical medical officers would also be excluded from membership of the Faculty. The Faculty was anxious to define community medicine as different from and complementary to clinical medicine and was therefore opposed to community physicians undertaking clinical practice,[13] especially when clinic duties were considered to be dull, routine and low status. The Hunter Report stated clearly that specialists in community medicine would not be personally involved in the clinical work of the personal health services. In common with many subsequent documents, it was vague as to the future of such work:

A significant part of the clinical work will no doubt continue to be performed for some time to come by the doctors currently employed on clinical work by local authorities, often on a part-time basis . . . . There is a trend towards greater participation by GPs in these services which we welcome and hope will continue.[14]

The Court Report had recommended that child health work be transferred to GPs[15] and this position was endorsed by the Royal Colleges and the General Management Services Committee of the BMA, as well as the Faculty. But the CMOs have continued to struggle for specialized training and a career structure through the Central Committee on Community Medicine of the BMA, which has tended to see them as valuable allies of the small and rather isolated group of community physicians. While their demands for specialist status as a 'third force' have been rejected, the Royal Colleges have acknowledged their need for a training programme.[16]

Third, there were the MOsH of large county and county borough councils who already earned a consultant's salary and who found that after 1974 they lost control of their administrative staff, nurses and public health inspectors. In areas and districts where it proved difficult to fill SCM posts, some found that they had to turn their hands to tasks subordinates had done previously, in environmental health, for example.[17] From their survey of community physicians in

1977, W.H. Parry and J.E. Lunn reported that a large majority felt that they had suffered a loss of responsibility as a result of reorganization.[18] In fact, their field of responsibility had been broadened dramatically. What the response reflected was the difficulty MOsH experienced in adjusting to the internal structure of community medicine and the new ways of working. Senior MOsH had to accept hitherto junior colleagues as equals and to change their methods of working from an executive to a consensus management style, as well as expanding their knowledge of their communities (which were in many cases new) to include the hospitals and general practice. Medical administrators with the hospital boards undoubtedly had the edge over MOsH in making the transition largely because they were used to the hospital culture and dealing with clinicians.

During an interview with one DMO (formerly an AMO and MOH) he took a 'wrong number' telephone call, which caused him to remark grimly that when he was MOH he was 'God' and no one would have called his office by mistake. The chagrin of these senior men was compounded when they discovered that in many areas 'real power' in the 1974–82 structure lay at district level, largely because hospital consultants had always been used to operating at the level of the district general hospital. The vast majority of former MOsH were highly committed to unification of the NHS because they felt it would be good for the service, because many were dissatisfied with local authority control of the public health service, and because all welcomed the move to specialist status. However, one of my respondents reported that as early as 1975 substantial disaffection was expressed at a meeting of community physicians in his region because they had seriously underestimated the nature of the change, particularly in respect of the loss of their executive authority. One respondent felt that he had worked hard on the Joint Liaison Committee, which planned the 1974 reorganization and had virtually put the new structure in place single-handedly, only to find that he then had 'no service to run'. This bears out Brown's observations of Humberside, where MOsH played a major part in the reorganization but where they appeared to have little opportunity in the new structure to take a leadership role.[19]

Those senior people experiencing greatest difficulty in adjusting tended to take early retirement in 1982 (this amounted to 20 per cent of the total number of community physicians). Because of this large number of early retirements there were enough jobs to go round in 1982, despite an overall cut in the number of posts. There was nevertheless anxiety. One SCM respondent reported that she felt additional pressure knowing that the refuge of general practice was closed because it too required specialist training by 1982. There was also a 'different psychology' to the restructuring in 1982. Compared with 1974 there was little information or reassurance from the DHSS, and more suspicion and cynicism among NHS personnel. Much more local discretion was permitted in the second reorganization. Policies on early retirement and whether the new posts would be filled by slotting-in or by regional competition varied between regions. In addition, the competition in 1982 was for jobs that could be perceived to 'belong' to a particular individual. Finally, anxiety was caused by the length of time some Regions took to make their final arrangements and notify community physicians of their decision as to whether posts would be filled by competition and the number of SCM posts that would be filled. (The BMA suggested that the number of SCM posts be worked out according to the formula: one DMO and one SCM per 100,000 population, plus a half-time SCM post per district and an additional half-time post for teaching districts.)[20] In the case of one respondent, the delay in the decision over staffing arrangements occasioned a move to another district in order to be sure of a post.

Former MOsH of large areas who remained in post underwent what many of them perceived as another demotion in 1982 from AMO to DMO, for the status of the MOH had always been measured in terms of the population served. Those who had been DCPs and became DMOs tended to be more satisfied, believing that the 1982 restructuring vindicated the district concept and the view of many that the substantive work of community medicine had been done at district level between 1974 and 1982. However, a DCP who became a DMO but who found that his fellow district management team members all came from the old area was likely to experience some difficulties.

Thus reorganization represented a major upheaval in human terms that was insufficiently acknowledged both before and after the event. Perhaps not surprisingly many community physicians attempted to make their new jobs resemble their old ones as much as possible. In 1978 Dr D. Patey, DCP for Bury St Edmunds, reported being 'shocked' to hear at a conference that one DCP in a teaching district continued to concern himself only with running the former local health authority services.[21] In two districts I visited, the former secretary of the hospital management committee had become the administrator and the MOH the community physician, and by tacit agreement they continued to manage their districts in such a way that both continued to do virtually the same jobs as before reorganization. Many SCMs found it easier still to continue the traditional work of a public health doctor, supervising personal health services, liaising with local authorities and taking responsibility for communicable disease control. Many older SCMs who made the transition to community medicine in 1974 identified more closely with the clinical medical officers than with other community physicians. However, many recruits to the specialty after 1974 felt that such work had little to do with the practice of community medicine. Rather, they were concerned that community physicians should have the opportunity to combine population medicine with higher status clinical work. Of 149 people training for the Faculty's membership examinations in 1978, 73 per cent felt that the option to practise clinical medicine would have positive effects on recruitment to the specialty.[22] Both SCMs (Environmental Health) and those DCPs who took on the job of 'Proper Officer' found that the demands made of them by local authorities often increased. The DCP for Blackpool, for example, served as Proper Officer to three local authorities for which he had to undertake 883 medical examinations (for new staff) and assess 946 applications for rehousing in a year.[23] Such jobs bore little resemblance to the kind of epidemiological research and planning and evaluation tasks envisaged by academics and policy-makers for the community physician. Indeed, a substantial minority of former public health doctors continued to express their allegiance to their former roles and tasks through their membership of the Society of Community

Medicine, formerly the Society of Medical Officers of Health.

Just as it was difficult for older public health doctors to make the conscious effort that was often needed to change their whole approach to their work, so it was also difficult for many to adjust to the new working relationships within the specialty. The world of the public health doctor had been severely hierarchical. Community physicians on the other hand were to enjoy equal specialist status. However, there was a clearly perceived status hierarchy running from RMO through AMO to DCP and SCM. SCMs at region enjoyed a higher cachet than SCMs at area and quite possibly also than DCP. In 1982 one of my respondents, who was appointed AMO in 1974, preferred to take a job as SCM at region, which he regarded as a lateral move, to a post as DMO, which he perceived as a demotion.

Former MOsH who became AMOs experienced considerable difficulty in working with SCMs when they could not direct their work. In a few cases SCMs continued the pattern of the public health department and worked to the DMO. Two of my respondents openly stated that they felt a good administrator working to them would be worth more than an SCM. Writing in 1978, S. Green, a lecturer at St Thomas's, referred to situations in which SCMs responsible for liaising with local authorities on social services found themselves alienated from their AMOs and formed working relationships only with colleagues in the social services departments.[24] Respondents also provided examples of DCPs who had refused to recognize the 'sapiential authority' of SCMs working at area and who would deal only with the AMO; and of AMOs who treated DCPs as their subordinates.[25] One commented that community physicians 'had sold their hierarchical heritage for a mess of consultancy', and another that 'unless you can actually deploy something in the way of resources there's actually very little influence you can have'. Such comments do pinpoint one of the essential weaknesses of community medicine. In 1974 the community physician faced an expanded range of responsibilities, more often than not with little or nothing in the way of staff to assist. Furthermore, unlike other members of the management team, the community physician was forced to rely entirely on the quality of the advice he/she could bring to hear, community physicians being numerically insignificant.

Forging the role of the community physician
From the beginning, community physicians found the 'community hat' a difficult one to wear. As Dr G.R. Brackenridge, DCP for Northallerton, pointed out in 1981, while the Royal Commission on Medical Education had proposed that the term community 'should embrace the whole population, whether living at home, in institutions or in hospitals of a given geographical area . . . in practice, the opposite has happened: at all levels and within all disciplines of the health service the adjective "community" is almost invariably used to describe the "non-hospital" health services'.[26] Thus while it was intended that the community physician should provide the necessary 'intelligence' for adjudicating the resource needs of various types of health services including the hospital, in practice the title community physician often meant that other members of the management teams expected him to speak for the community services outside the hospital. In many respects the division between hospital services and those provided outside the hospital was a useful one from the point of view of administrators. Community physicians also found that many clinicians continued to assume that their role remained essentially that of an MOH. On the other hand the battle to come to terms with the problems of the hospital service meant that many community physicians who continued to feel considerable commitment to the extra-hospital health services and to the work of prevention and promotion, felt that their work was determined more by the needs of the NHS than those of communities they served. Thus the position of community physicians was subject to serious conflicts in terms both of their relationship with other members of the medical profession, and the nature of their primary responsibility, whether for the management of health services or for the analysis of health problems and health needs.

COMMUNITY PHYSICIANS AND THE MEDICAL PROFESSION

In 1974 community physicians were granted specialist status

equal to that of clinicians. However, few clinicians understood the nature or internal structure of the new specialty. As the *Lancet* commented in 1974, 'the old public health image of community medicine dies hard'.[27] Among my respondents one young DMO described the clinician's lack of understanding and respect for community medicine in his district ten years after the establishment of the specialty as 'galling', and five others referred to their need to proceed with the utmost caution, 'to creep along' in the words of one, for 'fear of upsetting clinicians'. Perhaps it is not surprising that 68 per cent of the community medicine trainees surveyed by Acheson in 1979 thought that the option to practise personal clinical medicine would strengthen the credibility of the specialty and 'improve relationships with other specialties'.[28]

Many former MOsH experienced difficulties in dealing with clinicians on district management teams (DMTs) and in the medical advice machinery. In the case of the latter, many clinicians persisted in turning to the community physician in his position on the management team rather than as a specialist in population medicine. The district medical committees set up in 1974 were intended to replace the medical executive committees set up as a result of the first 'Cogwheel' Report on the organization of medical work in hospitals,[29] but, as S. Haywood and A. Alaszewski noted in their 1980 study, few district medical committees proved strong enough to replace the MECs.[30] Furthermore, the position of community medicine has proved extremely weak within the Cogwheel medical advice machinery. As members of a new specialty, many community physicians felt insecure in the presence of the clinical colleagues and their standing was not improved by the publicity accorded the poor examination results of students sitting the Faculty's examinations in 1977.[31] R. Schultz and S. Harrison's study of members of 19 area management teams in 1981 found that AMOs were the most influential team members in only three of the cases and the least in eight. Those exerting little influence were also found to be the least clear about their aims and objectives; to have little information to draw upon; and to speak platitudinously about the problems they faced.[32] Two of my respondents confessed to lacking confidence in their ability to deal with colleagues on the management team and to remaining silent whenever hospital-related problems were discussed. Not only do clinicians tend to be more vocal on management teams, but from their study Schultz and Harrison concluded, like Haywood and Alaszewski before them, that the real influence over health service management rested not so much with the management team as with the clinicians as a group within the NHS.[33]

Clinicians were also deeply suspicious of what community physicians were intended to do. The idea that community physicians should look at the health needs of the district and allocation of resources across the whole spectrum of the NHS would have led to difficulties in relations with other members of the medical profession at the best of times, for, as Gill pointed out, their role could easily be 'interpreted as an additional mechanism for increasing the accountability of the profession through internal review and evaluation'.[34] But during the mid-1970s, when severe financial restraints were imposed on the NHS, the position of the community physician became considerably more difficult. Alwyn Smith, professor of epidemiology and social oncology at the University of Manchester and president of the Faculty, summed up the difficulties this presented for the community physician: 'The community physician faces an agonising choice between becoming primarily an administrative assistant to his clinical colleagues or seeming to advocate a curtailment of his activities and resources.'[35] In a bitter article explaining why he was leaving the practice of community medicine in Britain, A. Griew, the DCP for Hereford and Worcester, wrote:

community medicine is at the bottom of the medical hierarchy. We are not regarded as physicians with the diagnostic skills of epidemiology, available to assist clinicians in improving their services. Rather we are snoopers, right hand men to administrators and finance officers in medically justifying their (supposedly) arbitrary decisions.[36]

Probably many clinicians saw in the community physician shades of the medical superintendent of the 1930s, whose administration of the work of the hospitals had been so detested.[37]

The image of the community physician as primarily a part of

the NHS management structure was reinforced when in 1976 community medicine posts were included in the review of management costs.[38] For Griew this proved the last straw: 'The Management Review was a major blow to my morale. I am a physician with managerial duties, and the inclusion of my staff in the review gives me no hope for the development of my specialty.'[39] Community physicians were not slow to point out that pre-1974 there were over 1,000 full-time posts in local authorities and regional hospital boards in England and Wales, but only 737 community medicine posts in the new structure and of these 15 per cent remained unfilled in 1976.[40] There was therefore a real chance that the imposition of a further cut would threaten the survival of the specialty. The Faculty's response was to appeal to the Ministry for a reprieve on the grounds that community physicians should be considered first and foremost specialists within the mainstream of medicine, but if they denied community medicine's administrative and management role too strongly, they risked a situation whereby community physicians would be demoted to the position of advisor to lay administrators. If community medicine defined itself as being primarily management oriented it risked offending clinicians, but if it did not its *raison d'être* in the eyes of government disappeared.

The difficulties inherent in the relationship between community physicians and clinicians became all too clearly visible in the 1978 Report of the Committee of Inquiry into Normansfield Hospital, where a consultant had been guilty of gross dereliction of duty. The AMO involved chose to leave the task of making administrative contact with the consultant to the administrative member of the management team. The Committee of Inquiry commented that while the AMO 'urged upon us that he personally had little if anything to answer for regarding the facilities at Normansfield', they 'emphatically' disagreed and pointed 'to the almost negligible part in the area management team's activities he seems to have played'. They concluded that he:

presented for our consideration a restricted and, we believe, unrealistic view of his role as AMO but it is hard to accept that he really held such views at the time of the events in question. We have reached the conclusion that to protect himself from criticism he chose to give an imprecise description of his role and to justify this by saying that the impression stemmed from the description of his duties and responsibilities as set out in 'Management Arrangements for the Reorganisation of the NHS' (the Grey Book). While we realise that the role of community physician is a rapidly evolving one in which all the precise functions and nuances are still somewhat flexible, we do not believe the 'Grey Book' to be as 'grey' in this respect as Dr. Nelson [the AMO] suggested.[41]

Thus the Committee accepted not only that the community physician's role was clearly set out, but that it was appropriate for the AMO in what was not a teaching area to inquire into the performance and activities of a consultant, who was, of course, employed by the RHA. Nor did it accept that the community physician might have difficulty in getting the information he needed if indeed he chose to pursue his inquiries.[42] Neither assumption was entirely justified and both risked prejudging future relations between clinicians and community physicians.

THE TASKS OF THE COMMUNITY PHYSICIAN

When community physicians took up their posts in 1974 the vast majority experienced great difficulty in defining their role and tasks. In a series of articles published in the *BMJ* in 1976, community physicians complained of having to face in too many different directions. DCPs catalogued their tasks as follows: management responsibilities to the DMT; health care planning, including assessment of service needs and the evaluation of services; the co-ordination of preventive services in the districts; and the provision of advice to GPs, consultants and local authorities, including, in the case of the latter, Proper Officer duties.[43] The core task of health care planning was one in which few MOsH who made the transition to community medicine had experience, nor did they have sufficient staff to obtain the necessary information. As Alwyn Smith noted, management teams expected community physicians to have 'an encyclopaedic knowledge of epidemiology which relatively few practising community physicians have had the opportunity to acquire'.[44] One of my respondents commented that he had expected 'to take a step back and become a commentator and a planner', but in practice he ended up getting 'heavily involved in the hurly burly'.

The Faculty and the BMA's Central Committee for Community Medicine (CCCM) identified three major aspects of the community physician's role: that of specialist, manager and advisor.[45] In theory these linked together easily: using specialist skills to establish patterns of health and illness, and health care needs in the community, the community physician advised his colleagues on policies (on the balance to be achieved between acute and chronic care, and the attention that should be given to prevention and promotion) and on the balance of spending that best matched his findings, arguing his case as a member of the management team. The Faculty has always tended to stress the specialist advisor role of the community physician. When J.N. Morris spoke in 1968 about the future of community medicine, he did not speak favourably of a possible management component in the community physician's task: 'I hope to goodness in the health service we don't go crazy on this notion of management, this magic word . . . which as yet doesn't have an awful lot in it.'[46] However those community physicians with places on the formal management structure found (as the policy documents of 1972 intended that they should) that they here pulled towards a management role. In 1977 one community physician expressed disappointment that so few in the specialty had been able to fulfil the role sketched out by Morris in the late 1960s, and he blamed the way in which community medicine 'had been subordinated to institutionalized management'.[47]

To perform both the specialist/advisor and management tasks effectively required the community physician to face in a number of different directions which his training, personal inclinations and opportunities did not permit. Furthermore, the fact that not all community physicians have a formal place on management teams was bound to result in differing interpretations of the prescription given to community medicine. As a specialty community medicine could not afford to jeopardize its credibility in the eyes of the medical profession by being too closely associated with the NHS bureaucracy. Yet community medicine's positions were deeply embedded in the new structure of the NHS. Community physicians were intended to 'manage'; moreover, if they did not, their numbers and status were such that it was by no means clear that the advice they could offer would be followed. Some of the more recent comments by academic members of the Faculty have sought to re-emphasize community medicine's primary task to provide specialists in population medicine with experience in epidemiology, fearing that, in the words of W. Holland, 'too much time has been spent in developing committee and management structures, rather than in developing its own skills'.[48] Holland urged community physicians to become change agents by power of persuasion grounded in expert knowledge. However, in practice many community physicians found that the practicalities of their position did not permit them to steer clear of the politics of health service affairs. Any advice on the appropriate balance of health service provision, which Holland acknowledged as one of the aims of the specialty, inevitably involved the community physician in medical and health service politics.

Community physicians were given little preparation for their new management roles in the NHS. Their understanding of their tasks in this respect was often vague and their commitment ambivalent. As F. Eskin remarked, there remained considerable confusion over the distinction between administration and management.[49] One of the early complaints by community physicians was the amount of time they were spending on routine administration. One anonymous AMO complained that 'the work I am involved in I would have thought a second or a third tier administrator could deal with—certainly not somebody like myself'.[50] A survey by R.J. Donaldson and D.J. Hall of the work of community physicians, which asked all community physicians to keep a diary of their activities for a week at the end of 1977, found that 'administration in its several guises was the major activity, which in total, took up 60 per cent of ascribable time',[51] although it is not possible to tell from the survey how precisely community physicians were defining administration. Nevertheless it is entirely probable that a majority of those community physicians who had been former MOsH devoted more attention to the day-to-day running of the service—especially the community health services—than to collaborating with other disciplines on the preparation of health policy. This certainly applied to four of the twenty-seven community physicians with formal management responsibilities in my sample who continued to engage in virtually the same activities as prior to 1974.

In addition, the commitment of community medicine to playing a management role within the NHS bureaucracy was ambivalent, in part because the Faculty always stressed the primary importance of the community physician's specialist/advisor role and in part because of the division within community medicine between those community physicians with formal management responsibilities and those without. The King Edward's Hospital Fund for London Working Party on the Education and Training of Senior Managers in the NHS commented on the tension between two aspects of management: the professional (meaning the responsibility to take a leadership role within the discipline) and the team approach to policy-making.[52] M. Dixon and A. Metz's 1981 study of chief officers of management teams found community physician members of management teams to be the most clearly defined, homogeneous groups, expressing a preference for further training in specifically health-related courses, despite the low percentage who had attended management courses.[53] Thus it might be expected that the kind of tension described by the King's Fund Working Party would be particularly acute in their case. Indeed the Working Party commented that 'there is still uncertainty at the level of senior manager upon the issue of the extent to which the community medicine specialist in the management team becomes a corporate manager as well as an epidemiologist'.[54]

In practice, the community physician usually found the struggle to combine the roles of specialist advisor and manager in the manner originally outlined by the Faculty impossible. In 1979 the Duncan Report instigated by the Community Medicine Craft Conference and supported by the Faculty and the BMA's CCCM concluded that two types of career appointment in community medicine were necessary: the SCM whose role was primarily that of specialist, and the community physician who concentrated on fulfilling his formal management responsibilities.[55] A similar conclusion was reached by the research team investigating the working of the health service for the Royal Commission on the NHS which reported in 1979.[56] The Duncan Report refrained from going so far as to say that these were two separate strands in community medicine, but others were not so circumspect. N.S. Galbraith, an AMO, argued strongly from 1976 for two distinct types of community medicine post—managerial and epidemiological—because in his view epidemiology had been eclipsed by the management tasks demanded by the new NHS structure.[57] The opposite view was taken by S. Cang, a researcher with the Brunel Institute of Organization and Social Studies, who felt that the community physician had been too preoccupied with developing his specialist role. Cang argued that the core of community medicine was administration. Epidemiology was a research activity more appropriate to a university department. He recommended that the community physician concentrate on administering the work of doctors.[58] This idea was singularly insensitive to the careful balancing act practised by the Faculty, and abhorrent to most community physicians who made it clear that they had no desire to administer the work of other doctors.[59] Nevertheless, his ideas were probably more in line with the intentions of the planning documents of 1972 than were the Faculty's. Certainly Lord Hunter, who had chaired the 1972 Committee on Medical Administrators, spoke in 1979 of his regret that the authority of the community medicine to dictate the pattern of resource allocation had not been more firmly established, thus making clear his personal view that in 1972 the management role of the community physician had been the priority.[60] Not surprisingly the Faculty insisted that the activities of management and the provision of advice were inseparable and only became divided in the hands of politicians.[61] The *Lancet* also agreed that it was dangerous to divide the new specialty, maintaining that all should receive the basic training in community medicine with certain people being selected for management training.[62]

This did not stop divisions developing between community physicians with management responsibilities and those without. Six of the twenty-seven community physicians with management responsibilities whom I interviewed felt that SCMs were reluctant to bear equal responsibility in a crisis. In other words they felt the management role also implied a hierarchical relationship. The eighteen SCMs in their turn tended to be critical of the time the DMOs devoted to management tasks, although the five more recently trained appreciated the necessity for a management component in community medicine. However, very few community physicians with management responsibilities were able, because of both inadequate training and practical pressures and constraints, to contribute to the management teams in the manner described by the Faculty. Most relied on manipulative skills, exercised both formally and informally, and considered that intensive epidemiological research was unnecessary. As one put it,

the anomalies you encounter are so gross that you don't really need expert specialist knowledge to conclude that you've got too many to too few beds or that the elderly aren't getting a fair deal or that your family planning services are non-existent or that there are far too many inappropriate terminations of pregnancy.

There is some evidence that community medicine trainees entering the specialty since 1974 have been uneasy about taking posts involving management responsibilities. Certainly a survey in 1983 found that a majority expressed a preference for the job of SCM,[63] where it is easier to apply the specialist skills in epidemiology acquired in training.

The bulk of the community medicine literature published since 1974 has been devoted to the problem of defining community medicine's role and tasks with the issue of the community physician's management versus specialist/advisor role predominating. It may be argued that the terms of the debate have been structured by the position of the community physician within the NHS bureaucracy. The question revolves around whether the community physician should be satisfied with offering advice to his/her clinical and administrative colleagues or whether he/she should play an active role in health service politics. It is hard to see how this can be an 'either/or' issue, because political influence is essential for the implementation of policies. The argument is really about priorities and approach—those advocating the pre-eminence of the specialist advisor role also being those most concerned about the legitimacy of their specialty within the medical profession. However, there are community physicians who have raised much more fundamental questions about the relationship of the community physician to the NHS management structure and about the nature of his/her task.

Some community physicians have perceived a tension between the community physician's place in the formal management structure of the NHS and his/her responsibilities to speak on behalf of the community of health questions. A. Scott Samuel, an SCM, suggested in 1979 that while the community physician is accountable in terms of his/her management task to the NHS bureaucracy, ethically his/her responsibility lies to the people.[64] Another recent commentator has also raised the question of whether the community physician is accountable to the management team, health authority members or the community,[65] and in its submission to the Griffiths Inquiry on NHS Management, the Faculty stated its belief 'that the progressive decline in the accountability of the service to the communities it serves is unfortunate'.[66] Two community physicians I interviewed spoke forcefully of the need to make the community physician spokesman for the people's health; one of these felt that the community physician should be made accountable for community diagnosis, and the other felt that he/she should pay more attention to community health councils. This is an idea that has been explored in some detail recently. The Donaldson and Hall survey found that 33 per cent of the time community physicians spent on communication was taken up by interaction with NHS administrators and only 3 per cent with community health councils and the press.[67] As N. Black has pointed out, community physicians have tended to perceive the community as an entity for study rather than as a working partner.[68] Black traces the failure to co-operate with community health councils back to the Grey Book, but the attitudes he describes have longer antecedents than this. Neither MOsH nor academic departments of social medicine were in the habit of consulting community interests, although MOsH often worked alongside voluntary groups. Social medicine academics, who dominated the Faculty of Community Medicine from its inception, were prone to regard the community as the subject of its endeavours rather than as a partner. Only four of the forty-three community physicians in my sample raised the relationship between community medicine and the community health councils voluntarily, seeing them as the 'natural allies' of the community physician. The rest viewed them as either 'bland', 'bothersome', or 'managers *manqués*'. One DMO felt that they had been more important in the period between 1974 and 1982 when in many cases they had taken the district's part against the area team.

Closely allied to the question of the community physician's accountability to the community as opposed to the NHS bureaucracy has been the responsibility some community physicians feel to take up a broader mandate as spokespersons on the state of the people's health. Traditionally the MOH was expected to fullfil a 'watchdog' role, although it has been argued in previous chapters that by the late 1960s the vast majority were absorbed by the administration of services. Nevertheless, most of the community physicians I interviewed, particularly those who had been public health doctors prior to 1974, spoke of a commitment to prevention and a regret that prevention seems to get lost in the years following 1974. It was part of the general disillusionment in 1976 that community physicians found they had little time to devote to prevention.[69] One community physician with formal management responsibilities said, 'I completely underestimated the problems of the hospital services', and another felt that he had been forced to eschew all interest in prevention and the community health services to gain the right to speak about the hospitals.

It is not easy to pin down exactly what community physicians mean by prevention. Those who made the transition to community medicine in 1974 continued to define prevention in terms of the personal and environmental health services delivered by the MOH. However, the expression of concern about prevention also serves to signal the community physician's unease about the amount of time that is absorbed by managing the health service rather than by analysing health problems. In the Faculty's own definition of community medicine, prevention tends to occupy at best an 'equal first' position. For example, in a 1977 document the Faculty states the specialty's 'continuous commitment above all, to positive

action in the promotion of health and prevention of disease',
but goes on to list the concerns of community medicine as
promotion and prevention, and the assessment of the
community's health needs and the provision of services.[70] In
practice there is little doubt but that the latter had
predominated. The definition of prevention in the Faculty and
the BMA's CCCM documents has in any case been a limited
one. When Morris talked about 'integrating' prevention and
cure in the late 1960s, he was thinking of prevention primarily
in terms of the individual or 'lifestyle' approach later
publicized further by the Canadian Lalonde Report, followed
in Britain by *Prevention and Health: Everybody's Business* and
the attention devoted to prevention by the 1979 Royal
Commission on the NHS.[71] In 1981, the BMA's CCCM listed
immunization, screening, the mitigation of existing chronic
conditions and the prevention of further disability and
handicap, the provision of information on environmental
hazards, and education in healthy lifestyles as the major
components of the community physician's preventive task. It
thus combined the new individual approach with specific
elements of the former MOH's responsibilities. While the
community physicians I interviewed, the vast majority of
whom had made the transition to community medicine in 1974,
thought of prevention almost solely in terms of the latter, five
younger recently trained SCMs spoke of prevention solely in
terms of 'lifestyle' and believed it to be properly the work of the
GP. Community physicians in their view should concentrate
on epidemiology only as a means to planning, not prevention.

Three community physicians I spoke to wished that their
responsibility for 'community diagnosis'—the analysis of
health problems and health needs—could be made clearer.
This indicated a rather broader concept of prevention,
incorporating a direct responsibility for the wider environmental issues affecting health along the lines recognized in 1979 by
the Guy's Unit for the Study of Health Policy.[72] The Black
Report on Health Inequalities went further still in calling for a
'total and not merely a service-oriented approach to the
problems of health', to include the improvement of all aspects
of the material conditions of life for poorer groups, and a
'radical overhaul of the balance of activity and proportionate

distribution of resources within the health and associated services' in favour of prevention and community health.[73] As the editors of the Pelican edition of the Report (P. Townsend and N. Davidson) recognized, such recommendations amount to 'a political and medical minefield'.[74] The secretary of state for social services dismissed the Report as recommending an 'unrealistic' increase in public expenditure and within the Black Working Group itself division arose between doctors and social scientists as to whether acute services should or could be cut back in favour of prevention.[75]

Academic members of the Faculty of Community Medicine viewed the implications of the move to broaden community medicine's mandate in respect to prevention with unease. In a review of the Guy's Unit document, W. Holland commented, 'The Unit considers that the specialty should be "concerned with the problems of medicine and society" . . . . This is a very wide definition indeed and suggests that community medicine should be a highly politicized subject.'[76] This was not an appealing prospect to a Faculty still seeking to legitimize its position within the medical profession, and Holland pleaded for 'unbiased work' and for community physicians to advise their administrative and clinical colleagues by taking 'a stand on objective evidence rather than on that of opinion'.[77] Yet in many respects this seemed only to fudge the issue. For in a sense any stand taken by the community physician is inevitably 'political'. As the Faculty itself noted in its submission to the Griffiths Inquiry, 'while clinicians usually advocate such change [in behaviour] for individuals, community physicians are inescapably involved in the advocacy of social and political change'.[78] Community physicians were intended to play a mediating role in the restructured NHS and their very position within the NHS bureaucracy has made it difficult to be perceived as offering 'neutral' advice. If the mandate of community medicine is broadened to focus on health problems rather than health services, then the community physician is likely to get involved in health service and medical politics involving issues of resource distribution and social justice. In fact, public health has never been in a position to claim such a broad mandate for itself and has never had such a wide remit during the twentieth century.

COMMUNITY MEDICINE IN THE 1980s

The policy documents of 1972 gave the community physician a pivotal role to play in the effective integration of the new helath service, and it has been argued that the role of the community physician was determined in large part by the place he occupied in the new NHS structure. However, the policy documents of the 1980s—*Patients First*, which signalled a second reorganization of the health service, and the Griffiths Report on management in the NHS—have shown little awareness or appreciation of the community physician's contribution. As a result the position of community medicine is currently uncertain.

By the 1980s integration of the health service was no longer the focus of attention and the concept of management had shifted away from the achievement of consensus towards a more straightforward preoccupation with careful administration and clear lines of accountability. *Patients First* made no mention of community medicine's contribution and the emphasis was clearly on better management of the hospitals. As the Outer Circle Policy Unit noted, services outside the hospital were 'in danger of being regarded as an appendage to the hospital service', and indeed 'from the time of *Patients First*, it appears that the government would welcome a return to pre-1974 "simplicity", when the hospital service formed the core of the NHS'.[79] In fact, while the document exhibited remarkably little concern about the community care services which had been declared a priority in government documents of the 1970s,[80] its preoccupation with the hospitals was explained not so much by desire to make them the centrepiece of the NHS as to find a way of containing their spiralling costs. Between 1950 and 1977, hospitals increased their share of NHS expenditure from a half to two-thirds; spending on prevention accounted for only 0.2 per cent of the NHS budget in 1979–80.[81]

Patients First suggested that by removing the area tier the NHS bureaucracy would become more responsive to local needs. However, the emphasis placed on the importance of local management and decision-making was designed to increase the efficiency of the service rather than local accountability. Indeed the consultative document suggested that community health councils might no longer be necessary. The document stressed the importance of delegating authority to the local level, but in the event, as Klein has pointed out, the 1982 restructuring was followed by the first systematic attempt in the history of the NHS to call the health authorities to account by annual scrutiny of the work of district health authorities and the use of performance indicators.[82] The basic idea expressed in *Patients First* was that if the structure and management of the NHS 'are not right then nothing else will work properly',[83] which was essentially the same philosophy as had informed the Seebohm reorganization and the 1974 organization of the health service.

The idea of yet another structural fix evoked a gloomy response from community physicians. Professor R. Logan asked if this were Dunkirk and saw the risk of 'disintegration, of separating hospital from community and of neglect of prevention and evaluation'.[84] S. Horner, the chairman of the BMA's CCCM, saw the prospect of 'exile into Babylon'.[85] In fact, the outcome of the second reorganization was not as bad as these predictions feared, although the effect of another restructuring on the morale of a new specialty forced yet again into open competition for jobs should not be underestimated, especially when the number of community physician posts was decreased. Most of the community physicians I spoke to who had a formal management role in the health service felt more at ease in their positions after 1982. Despite the feeling among some former AMOs that the change in title to DMO involved a loss of status,[86] the majority of the twenty-seven DMOs I spoke to stressed the advantages that accrued from concentrating managerial authority in the DMO. In the words of one, the DMO represented 'the clear backstop' and he felt that his new position amounted to more than a simple combination of the duties of the AMO and the DCP. The removal of the area tier simplified relationships within community medicine, but also resulted in greater polarization between the management and specialist/advisor strands within the specialty. The division between DMOs with formal management responsibilities and SCMs without became clearer still.

Furthermore, the development of unit management teams

and the devolution of planning and financial authority to the new units also posed problems for community medicine.[87] Where community units were formed it was usual for the SCM to sit on the UMT as the medical representative, although three of the sixteen SCMs I interviewed had resisted this development because they felt it undermined community medicine's claim to analyse the provision of services inside and outside the hospital. As M. Dixon has pointed out, the relationship between unit and district is complicated, one of the major problems being either that the district may work too far above the unit or that there may be overlap.[88] The community physician had to be prepared to work at both levels. The problems of a DMO and one or two SCMs dealing with a district dominated by a large teaching hospital, with perhaps a 'Cinderella' geriatric hospital, the problems of inner-city community health services and two local authorities with opposing views are overwhelming. A DMO facing just this mix of problems reported feeling more like a 'delegated dogsbody' than a 'change agent'.'

Community medicine as a specialty managed to ride out the storm of 1982, albeit without resolving the fundamental tensions in the role of the community physician, but the results of the Griffiths reorganization look like being considerably less ambiguous. Like *Patients First*, the Griffiths Report focused its attention firmly on the hospitals. In place of the complicated machinery necessary to achieve management through consensual planning, the Report recommended the appointment of a single general manager, readily identifiable at all levels. The trend away from the framework set up by the reorganization of 1974 is thus clear and it is therefore understandable that the main role of the community physician, central to the 1974 structure, has been eroded. If D. Gooding was right when she wrote in 1975 that integration was 'a philosophy not just an administrative rationalization',[89] then the preoccupation of the policy-makers of the 1980s with the hospital sector, and with a much narrower concept of management, has profound implications for community medicine.

The Griffiths Report itself was sufficiently vague not to provoke the kind of pessimistic response from community physicians that greeted *Patients First*. The Faculty of

Community Medicine welcomed the emphasis it put on achieving greater accountability and on involving consultants in management. An editorial in *Community Medicine* assured community physicians that they would continue to play a major role in the assessment of need, in planning and, most importantly, in the provision of information.[90] Only a small minority of the DMOs I interviewed just after the appearance of the Griffiths Report expressed interest in becoming general managers, fearing that they would become too closely associated with the NHS bureaucracy and lose credibility as physicians. Indeed the establishment of a chief executive had been rejected by the Grey Book which guided the 1974 organization, by the Royal Commission on the NHS in 1979, and by *Patients First*, as being incompatible with professional autonomy. As of September 1985, when 92 per cent of the appointments to the post of general manager had been made, some two-thirds were filled by people who had been administrators within the NHS. Only 9 per cent of 219 general manager posts in the UK were filled by DMOs.[91]

The appointment of general managers has raised serious questions about the direction of community medicine and in particular about the formal management role of community physicians. The Report of the House of Commons Social Services Review Committee on the Griffiths Inquiry spelled out clearly the possibility that the role of the DMO would undergo substantial change: 'should a general manager be appointed the role of the DMO and the consultant and the GP [on the management team] would be more purely advisory than it is at present'.[92] All my DMO respondents felt strongly that there was little point in diagnosing a problem if a solution could not be formulated and implemented. While community physicians have tended to make as much or more use of informal networks as formal channels, a diminution in the community physician's management role would nevertheless affect the specialty's visibility and status. R. Illsley has suggested that the relative invisibility of the community physician compared to the MOH has already proved problematic for the specialty.[93]

The DHSS Circular on implementing the Griffiths Report made it clear that the role of the DMO was likely to come to resemble that of the SCM more closely:

Professional Chief Officers are appointed by the authority and will continue to be directly accountable and have a right of access to the authority on the provision and quality of medical advice. On matters relating to the fulfilment of the general manager's responsibility, they will be accountable to the general manager for the day-to-day performance of their management functions.[94]

E.D. Acheson, the chief medical officer, interpreted this as a challenge to all community physicians to provide good medical advice.[95] In the wake of Griffiths it thus seems that the tension between community physicians' role as specialist advisors or managers will disappear, but that community medicine is in danger of becoming a service specialty. Even then it is by no means clear whether community physicians will have the resources to produce good medical advice; as of 30 September 1984 there were 15 DMO and 188 SCM posts vacant.[96] Nor is it clear that the general manager would seek advice from community physicians on health problems rather than from, say, health economists, lay administrators or planners, who may be well placed to perform the required service role at considerably less cost to the service.[97] Indeed, it seems that in twenty-eight of the ninety-two districts the 'Griffiths' management structures propose dropping medical officers from their new boards of management.[98] It may still be argued, along the original Hunter lines, that the value of the community physician lies in the fact that as a doctor he can talk to other doctors which suggests that community physicians may still be called in to advise and mediate on questions of evaluation and resource allocation. However, not only is their status likely to be lower in the eyes of their consultant colleagues as a result of the Griffiths reorganization, but this sort of role is a far cry from the greater involvement in prevention and the analysis of health problems that many community physicians seek.

In retrospect, it may be seen how the role of community physicians has been dominated by their place within the NHS structure. One of the fundamental problems faced by the NHS has always been the tension between public accountability and professional autonomy. In 1974 it was thought that the best way of reconciling these lay in the concept of consensus management and the community physician was placed in a key position within the new management structure. By the 1980s the prescription had changed and more hope was pinned on strong line administration and greater central control. The expectations of community medicine in 1974 were too high. As R.G.S. Brown put it, it was unrealistic to expect 'old wine' to be able to adjust overnight to 'new bottles'.[99] Older community physicians who had been MOsH had difficulty in coming to terms with their new roles. Moreover, a divide inevitably developed between them and the community physicians who were trained after 1974 and whose skills in epidemiology and planning were usually greater. This may be regarded as inevitable. Where the new specialty may be called to account is over its failure clearly to define its goals. Discussion centred on the role of the community physician rather than on goals, and tended to reinforce the division between the manager and specialist advisor roles, which was a product of the community physician's position in the new NHS structure. In practice, the community physician tended to be preoccupied with his responsibility to the health services rather than to health. The degree to which his position has been determined by the structure of the NHS is revealed in the aftermath of the Griffiths Report. For Griffiths sought to put new wine into new bottles (although in fact only a small minority of general managers came from the commercial sector) and the status of the community physician has been seriously eroded.

NOTES

1. DHSS Circular, 'Transition Arrangements: Interim Management Arrangements for Health Authorities', HRC (73) 36.
2. R.G.S. Brown, *Reorganizing the NHS: A Case Study in Administrative Change* (Oxford: Blackwell, 1979), p. 143.
3. For example, D.H. Stone, 'Is there a future for community medicine?', *BMJ*, II (1976), pp. 1086–8.
4. D. Gill, 'The reorganization of the NHS: some sociological aspects with special reference to the role of the community physician', in *The Sociology of the NHS*, Sociological Review Monograph, No. 22, ed M. Stacey (Keele: University of Keele, 1976).

5. D. Towell, 'Making reorganisation work: challenges and dilemmas in the development of community medicine', in *Conflicts in the NHS*, eds K. Barnard and K. Lee (London: Croom Helm, 1977).
6. A. Smith, 'The role of community medicine', in *Management for Health Service Administrators*, eds D. Allen and J.A. Hughes (London: Pitman, 1983).
7. DHSS and Welsh Office, *Patients First: Consultative Paper on the Structure of the NHS in England and Wales* (London: HMSO, 1979); and DHSS, *Report of the NHS Management Inquiry* (London: HMSO, 1983).
8. Brown, *Reorganizing the NHS*, p. 183.
9. J. Dearlove, *The Reorganisation of British Local Government: Old Orthodoxies and a Political Perspective* (Cambridge: Cambridge University Press, 1979); and R.J. Haynes, *Organization Theory and Local Government* (London: Allen & Unwin, 1980).
10. DHSS Circular, 'Filling of Senior Posts in RHAs and AHAs in England', NHSSA C 2/73, April 1973.
11. DHSS Circular, 'Personnel: Appointments Procedure for Posts in Community Medicine', HRC (73), 39, November 1973.
12. NHSSA C2/73 describes this procedure.
13. Faculty of Community Medicine, *Community Medicine and the Community Physician* (London: Faculty of Community Medicine, 1977).
14. DHSS, *Report of the Working Party on Medical Administrators* (London: HMSO, 1972), para. 75.
15. P.P., 'Fit for the Future: Report of the Committee on Child Health Services', Cmnd, 6684, 1976.
16. The debate over the future of the clinical medical officers may be followed in: BMA, CCCM, *Report of the Working Party on Community Health Doctors* (London: BMA, 1978); BMA, CCCM, Joint Paediatric Committee of the Royal College of Physicians and the British Paediatric Association, *Report on Clinical Medical Officers in the Child Health Service* (Faculty of Community Medicine, 1979).
17. DHSS Circular, 'Building up Community Medicine Establishment', CMO 5/74, March 1974.
18. W.H. Parry and J.E. Lunn, 'The community physician: will he survive?', *BMJ*, II (1977), pp. 589–90.
19. Brown, *Reorganizing the NHS*, p. 193.
20. BMA, CCCM, *Community Medicine at District in the Reorganised NHS, 1981–82* (London: BMA, 1981), para. 10.3.
21. D. Patey, 'What role the community physician?', *Health and Social Services Journal*, 17 February 1978, pp. 192–3.
22. E.D. Acheson, 'Clinical practice and community medicine', *BMJ*, II (1979), p. 880.
23, A. Jewsbury, 'The role of the community physician in the district', in *What Do Community Physicians Do?*, Occasional Paper No. 1 (Manchester: Unit for Continuing Education, Department of Community Medicine, University of Manchester, 1978), p. 32.
24. S. Green, 'The aspects of collaboration', *Health and Social Services Journal*, 8 August 1978, p. 1006.

25. *See also* G.S. Suthie, 'The DCP: a key role in the NHS', *Practice Team Compendium* (Nov./Dec. 1974), pp. 129–31.
26. G.R. Brackenridge, 'Community medicine: a revised prescription', *Public Health*, 95 (1981), p. 139.
27. 'Role of the community physician', editorial, *Lancet*, II (1974), p. 30.
28. Acheson, 'Clinical practice and community medicine', p. 880.
29. Ministry of Health, Joint Working Party, *First Report on the Organisation of Medical Work in Hospitals* (London: HMSO, 1967).
30. S. Haywood and A. Alaszewski, *Crisis in the NHS* (London: Croom Helm, 1980), p. 118.
31. 'Quality of applicants for community medicine posts abysmal says Professor', *Medical News*, 9 (1977), p. 2.
32. R. Schultz and S. Harrison, *Teams and Top Managers in the NHS* (London: King Edward's Hospital Fund for London, 1983).
33. *ibid.*; Haywood and Alaszewski, *Crisis in the NHS*.
34. Gill, 'The reorganization of the NHS', p. 20.
35. A. Smith, 'The role of community medicine', p. 120.
36, A. Griew, 'For reasons of health', *Health and Social Services Journal*, 28 January 1977, p. 155.
37. R.G.A. Shegog, 'Measureless to man', in *By Guess or By What?*, ed G. McLachlan (Oxford: University Press for Nuffield Provincial Hospitals Trust, 1978), p. 121.
38. DHSS Circular, 'Health Services Management: A Review of NHS Management', HC (76) 36, June 1976; 'Health Service Management: Review of Management Costs', HC (77) 10, April 1977.
39. Griew, 'For reasons of health', p. 155.
40. A.W. Macara, 'How can community medicine help the clinician?', *Community Medicine* 3 (1976), p. 46.
41. P.P., 'Report of the Committee of Inquiry into Normansfield Hospital', Cmnd. 7357, 1978, pp. 387–8.
42. W.J. Elwood and A.J. Lane, 'A North-Western Interpretation of the 'Normansfield' Report', in *The Community Physician as Manager*, Occasional Paper No. 3 (Manchester: Department of Continuing Education, Department of Community Medicine, University of Manchester, 1980).
43. A.R. Griew, J.P. Hutchby, A.K. Spence, M.C.T. Wilkes, 'Facing too many ways? Community medicine at district level', *BMJ*, II (1976), pp. 435–6.
44. Smith, 'The role of community medicine', p. 119.
45. Faculty of Community Medicine, 'Community medicine in the restructured NHS', *Community Medicine*, 3 (1981); and BMA, CCCM, *Community Medicine at District in the Reorganised NHS*.
46. J.N. Morris, 'The Specialty of Community Medicine', sessional paper given at a conference on 'Administrative Medicine and the Health Services of the Future', University of Aberdeen, 25 September 1968, tape held by the Wellcome Institute for the History of Medicine, CMAC Acc. No. 6.
47. M.F.H. Bush, letter, *BMJ*, II (1977), p. 956.

48. W. Holland, 'Community medicine—myth or change agent', *Journal of the Royal Society of Medicine*, 75 (1982), p. 846.
49. F. Eskin, 'The role of management training in community medicine', *Community Medicine* 1 (1979), pp. 236–42.
50. 'An AMO speaks', *Practice Team*, 27 (1974), p. 104.
51. R.J. Donaldson and D.J. Hall, 'The work of the community physician in England', *Community Medicine*, 1 (1979).
52. *Report of a Working Party on the Education and Training of Senior Managers in the NHS* (London: King Edward's Hospital Fund for London, 1977).
53. M. Dixon and A. Metz, *Management Development for Chief Officers in the NHS*, King's Fund Project Paper No. 33 (London: King Edward's Hospital Fund for London, 1982).
54. *Report of a Working Party on the Education and Training of Senior Managers*, p. 46.
55. *Report of a Joint Working Party on the State of Community Medicine* (London: BMA, CCCM and Faculty of Community Medicine, 1979), para. 321.
56. Royal Commission on the NHS, *The Working of the National Health Service*, Research Paper No. 1 (London: HMSO, 1978).
57. N.S. Galbraith, 'What I would suggest to the Royal Commission: community medicine attitudes', *BMJ* II (1976), p. 805–6.
58. S. Cang, 'Doctors and the NHS', TS (Brunel Institute of Organization and Social Studies, Brunel University, 1978).
59. A. Scott Samuel, 'Views of an SCM: planning and information', in *What Should Community Physicians be Doing?*, Occasional Papers No. 2 (Manchester: Unit for Continuing Education, Department of Community Medicine, University of Manchester, 1979), and G. Page, D. Williams and J. Yates, 'Comments on the discussion paper "Doctors and the NHS"', TS (Birmingham: University of Birmingham Health Services Management Centre, 1978).
60. Lord Hunter of Newington, *Community Physicians/Clinical Administrators* (Birmingham: University of Birmingham, 1979).
61. 'Community medicine: a single discipline', editorial, *Community Medicine*, 3 (1981), pp. 1–2.
62. 'Community medicine', editorial, *Lancet*, I (1979), p. 860.
63. S. Adam, 'Trainees in community medicine—report of a survey', in *A Career in Community Medicine* (Manchester: Unit for Continuing Education, Department of Community Medicine, University of Manchester, 1983).
64. A. Scott Samuel, 'The politics of health', *Community Medicine*, 1 (1979), pp. 123–6.
65. R.D. Weir, 'The practice of community medicine', *Community Medicine*, 5 (1983), pp. 133–9.
66. 'The NHS and its administration', editorial, *ibid.*, p. 337.
67. Donaldson and Hall, 'The work of the community physician', p. 60.
68. N. Black, ' "How many divisions has the Pope?" Community medicine and community health councils', *Community Medicine*, 3 (1979),

pp. 314–19.
69. J. Jones, 'The community physician: a suitable role for preventive medicine', *Health and Social Services Journal*, 12 November 1976, pp. 2014–15.
70. Faculty of Community Medicine, *Community Medicine and the Community Physician*.
71. Health and Welfare, Canada, *New Perspectives on the Health of Canadians: A Working Document* (Ottawa: Queen's Printer, 1974); DHSS, *Prevention and Health: Everybody's Business* (London: HMSO, 1976); and 'Report of the Royal Commission on the NHS', Cmnd. 7616, 1979, paras 5.2–5.12.
72. Unit for the Study of Health Policy, *Rethinking Community Medicine* (London: USHP, Guy's Hospital, 1979).
73. P. Townsend and N. Davidson, eds, *Inequalities in Health* (Harmondsworth: Penguin, 1982), p. 16.
74. *ibid.*, p. 29.
75. *ibid.*, pp. 16–17.
76. W. Holland, 'Rethinking community medicine: a reflection', *Community Medicine*, 3 (1981), p. 41.
77. *ibid.*
78. 'The NHS and its administration', *Community Medicine*, 5 (1983), p. 340.
79. Outer Circle Policy Unit, 'Health first: a comment on Patients First', TS (1980). *See also* University of Leeds Nuffield Centre for Health Service Studies, 'Patients First: intentions and consequences', TS (1980); and G. Wistow and S. Fuller, *Joint Planning in Perspective*, Centre for Research in Social Policy (Loughborough University, 1983), p. 1.
80. DHSS, *Priorities for Health and the Personal Social Services in England: A Consultative Document* (London: HMSO, 1976); and *Priorities in Health and Social Services: The Way Forward* (London: HMSO, 1977).
81. K. Lee, 'Public expenditure: health services and health', in *Public Expenditure and Social Policy*, ed A. Walker (London: Heinemann, 1982), pp. 86–7; and C. Ham, *Health Policy in Britain* (London: Macmillan, 1982), p. 40.
82. R. Klein, 'The politics of ideology v. the reality of politics: the case of Britain's NHS in the 1980s', *Millbank Memorial Quarterly, Health and Society*, 62 (1984), p. 93.
83. DHSS and Welsh Office, *Patients First*, p. 4.
84. R. Logan, 'Is this Dunkirk?', *Community Medicine*, 2 (1980), pp. 95–6.
85. 'Report on the Community Medicine Conference: exile into Babylon', *BMJ*, II (1981), p. 323.
86. See above, p. 132.
87. D.K. Nicol, 'Problems of integration at district and unit levels', Working Paper No. 49, University of Manchester, 1981.
88. M. Dixon, 'The organization and structure of units', in *Effective Unit Management*, ed I. Wickings (London: King Edward's Hospital Fund for London, 1981).
89. D. Gooding, 'Community medicine', in *Specialized Futures*, ed I. Craft *et al.* (Oxford: Oxford University Press for the Nuffield Provincial

Hospitals Trust, 1975), p. 57.
90. W.J. McQuillan, 'Griffiths—the future for community physicians and community medicine', *Community Medicine*, 6 (1984), pp. 3–6.
91. 'NHS general manager appointments', *Health and Social Services Journal*, 12 August 1985, supplement.
92. House of Commons, Paper 209, Social Services Committee, 1983–4, *First Report* (London: HMSO, 1984).
93. R. Illsley, *Professional or Public Health: Sociology in Health and Medicine* (Oxford: Oxford University Press for the Nuffield Provincial Hospitals Trust, 1980).
94. DHSS Circular, 'Health Services Management Implementation of the NHS Management Inquiry Report', HC (84) 13, June 1984, para. 7.
95. E.D. Acheson, 'Medical advice and health policy', *BMJ*, I (1985), pp. 1447–8.
96. DHSS, *Community Medicine Staff—Posts with a Permanent Holder, England and Wales, 30 September 1983* (London: DHSS, 1984).
97. R. Klein made this point some six years ago. *See* L. Paine, *Thoughts on Thwaites: A Commentary on Management Training in the NHS* (London: King Edward's Hospital Fund for London, 1979), p. 23.
98. 'BMA protests loss of influence on NHS', *The Guardian*, 1 November 1985, p. 3.
99. The phrase is R.G.S. Brown's, *Reorganizing the NHS*, ch. 8.

5 What price community medicine?

When the concept of community medicine and the role of the community physician were under discussion during the early 1970s, there was some division of opinion as to whether the creation of the specialty marked a new departure. In Scotland, both Sir John Brotherston and the Gilloran Report on community medicine argued that it did not.[1] According to Brotherston, community medicine was 'the latest name for that ancient, honourable and essential responsibility which is concerned with the medicine and health of the group. This is public health with a new name and new opportunities'.[2]

It was, of course, necessary to reassure MOsH in particular about the major change they were facing. But there was also a sense in which academics in the field believed that public health had 'lost its way', having been diverted into the provision of personal preventive services during the early twentieth century. When the Faculty referred to the specialty's origins, it usually mentioned the nineteenth-century pioneers rather than the pre-1974 health departments. In 1981, for example, the journal, *Community Medicine*, referred to the views of Sir John Simon, who 'looked forward to the day when "statecraft and medical knowledge took counsel together for the health of the people"', and argued that the phrase could be applied to modern community medicine.[3] A majority of academics were strongly convinced that the pre-1974 public health departments could not be defended and that public health had to be reformed and revitalized. The hope was to raise the status of public health by providing a more rigorous training for community physicians based on epidemiology and to create a genuine specialty of population medicine that was immediately recognizable as significantly different from general practice and hospital medicine.

The thrust of the efforts to revitalize public health involved substantially broadening its mandate. Those who introduced new public health curricula in the 1960s under the rubric of medical administration, spoke of public health doctors as 'health strategists', and the Faculty of Community Medicine envisaged community physicians analysing patterns of health and illness, assessing needs and evaluating services. The conscious effort first to provide a coherent rationale for the practice of community medicine, and second, to give it a broad mandate, should be seen as a radically new departure. In the nineteenth century, public health work covered a range of activities, including environmental hazard and housing, but in the name of protecting the national health rather than improving the health of the people *per se*. In the early twentieth century the definition of health problems narrowed significantly and scientific advance in the form of bacteriology pushed public health towards personal preventive medicine. By the inter-war years, public health had built the foundations of a state medical service, which was impressive in and of itself but was not supported by any coherent philosophy of public health work. When the government and the rest of the profession refused to accept the state medical service of the 1930s as a model for the post-war NHS, public health doctors settled with some difficulty to the task of co-ordinating and administering community health services. The rationale for their work remained unclear and increasingly was challenged by GPs and social workers, as well as by academics in social medicine and social science departments. Despite Brotherston's protestations, community medicine had little in common with the old public health.

Yet such an attempt to broaden the mandate of community medicine inevitably had both political and medico-political implications.[4] First the task of analysing patterns of health and illness and health needs is likely to involve consideration of factors outside the scope of the NHS, such as work, environment, income and housing, In the last quarter of the twentieth century these are not usually thought of as health problems and for doctors to talk about them may require the abandonment of scientific neutrality. Second, the task of taking a holistic view of the NHS itself and assessing the best balance to be achieved between services means that community physicians run the risk of conflict with other members of the medical profession. H. Francis has suggested that 'community medicine should be not so much a specialty within medicine as the way in which health services should be ordered within a welfare state'.[5] But this requires both political will and a commitment by the profession to consider the health of the collectivity as well as of the individual, neither of which is evident.

In fact, little thought was given to the way in which community medicine would be practised in the new NHS and community physicians experienced considerable tension in reconciling first their responsibility for the management of health services with that of analysing health problems and, second, their formal accountability to the NHS bureaucracy with their ethical accountability to their communities. Their role was very much determined by their place in the new NHS structure. Furthermore they were loosely identified with the NHS bureaucracy in the minds of their medical colleagues, as a report on the difficulties of recruitment to the specialty recognized in 1980: 'The emergence of community medicine as a specialty in 1974, coinciding with the reorganization of the NHS, has led to its being associated with the less successful structural and management changes brought about at that time.'[6] This was, if anything, to underestimate the case. For the suspicion with which community physicians were regarded deepened as the financial crisis that began in the mid-1970s resulted in cost restraint, even though community medicine suffered more than most specialties in the financial cuts. The generally low morale of the health service, together with the confusion community physicians experienced in respect to forging their new role and the gulf that developed between the ideas and practices of those who made the transition to community medicine in 1974 and those who trained after that date, bred an atmosphere of uncertainty and insecurity in the specialty. This was exacerbated by the government's change in policy direction in respect to the management of the health service during the 1980s. Whereas public health doctors in 1948 started out demoralized but grew in confidence during the 1950s and early 1960s (aided by a climate of optimism and economic growth), community physicians began optimistically but rapidly became disillusioned.

Many commentators have voiced their disappointment with community medicine. Some, like the Guy's Health Policy Unit, have looked back to the MOH and the local public health department as providing a better model for community medicine practice.[7] In T. Heller's view, 'Prior to reorganisation, most of the people now employed as community physicians were MOsH, who were separate from the NHS and who could consider the health of the entire community rather than simply concern themselves with service considerations.'[8] This was theoretically true, but rarely the case in practice. It cannot be argued that the transition to community medicine was achieved at the expense of an enormously vigorous public health system. On the other hand, there is little to rejoice over in respect to the current state of community medicine. The post-Griffiths district management structures promise not only to reduce the community medicine establishment still further, but further to narrow the mandate of the community physician to planning and information, or evaluation and audit, for example. This poses a serious threat not only to community medicine as a specialty, but also to the health of the people. In this respect the price of eroding community medicine may be high.

In its comments on the Report on recruitment to community medicine in 1980, the *BMJ* noted the important role to be played by a group of doctors committed to health rather than the cure of disease or the delivery of health services:

Doctors and the public are just beginning to realize the importance in the last 100 years of the work of medical men and women whose primary interest has been the improvement of the health of the population as a whole. The 1974 reorganisation conferred on them, for the first time, the advantages of a position on the key committees where health policy ought to be decided. But had this opportunity been taken and have the energies of community physicians been correctly directed? The problem has been and remains to ensure that their career opportunities meet their deeply felt aspirations as doctors to making maximum use, for example, of their understanding of the natural history of disease and the opportunities that exist to prevent it. Do the roles listed for the community physician in the Hunter Report really meet this prescription? Where does the function of the community physician end and that of his colleagues on the district management team begin?[9]

The *BMJ* was right to call these fundamental questions. Unfortunately, since 1980, the vulnerability of community medicine to shifts in government policy motivated primarily by the concerns of health service management has become much clearer.

NOTES

1. Sir John Brotherston, 'The specialty of community medicine', *Royal Society of Health*, 93 (1973); and Scottish Home and Health Department, *Community Medicine in Scotland* (London: HMSO, 1973), p. 3.
2. Brotherston, 'Specialty of community medicine', p. 203.
3. 'Community medicine: a single discipline', editorial, *Community Medicine*, 3 (1981?, p. 1.
4. See above, p. 3.
5. H. Francis, 'Towards community medicine: the British experience', in *Recent Advances in Community Medicine*, ed A.E. Bennett (Edinburgh: Livingstone, 1978), p. 14.
6. *Recruitment to Community Medicine: Report of a Joint Working Group* (London: DHSS, 1980).
7. Guy's Unit for the Study of Health Policy, *Rethinking Community Medicine* (London: Guy's Unit, 1979).
8. T. Heller, *Restructuring the Health Service* (London: Croom Helm, 1978), pp. 78–9.
9. 'Community medicine: a second chance', editorial, *BMJ*, II (1980), p. 826.

Appendix I The public health responsibilities of local government, 1929–1974

Throughout this period, public health legislation placed particular obligations on the local sanitary authorities—i.e., the county councils, county borough councils and urban and rural district councils.

County Councils: Took responsibility for appointing a county medical officer of health and for paying all district councils one half of the salary of their medical officers and sanitary inspectors; for the appointment of analysts, for example under the Food and Drug Acts; for hospitals and for personal health services to mothers and children, VD and TB patients.

County Boroughs: Were 'all-purpose' authorities, taking responsibility for all the matters covered by both the county and rural and urban district councils.

Urban and Rural District Councils: These were primarily sanitary authorities, dealing with matters such as nuisances, drains, sewerage, refuse, food, water and building inspections. Before the NHS Act 1946 these authorities also bore responsibility for maternal and child welfare services. To the chagrin of district medical officers, the 1946 Act confined the districts strictly to the provision of sanitary services and made all local personal health services the responsibility of the county and county borough councils.

Sources: J.J. Clarke, *The Local Government of the UK* (6th edn; London: Pitman, 1931) and W.E. Jackson, *The Structure of Local Government in England and Wales* (5th edn; London: Longmans, 1967).

Index

academic social and community
    medicine 17, 35, 44, 58, 70,
    78, 100, 102–3, 113, 128, 160
    antagonism to 66
aftercare 47–8, 72
ambulance service 16, 46, 60
ante-natal care 31, 76
applied aetiology 37
applied physiology 6
area management teams 136–7
Area Medical Officers 128, 134,
    136, 138–9, 141, 143, 150
Association of County Medical
    Officers of Health 84
Association of Municipal
    Corporations 67
attachment schemes 72–3, 91

bacteriology 5, 6, 21, 161
bed shortages 58
Bevan, A. 46
Beveridge Report 37
Black Report 147
Bonham Carter Report 112
British Medical Association 24,
    46, 63
  Annual Representatives
    Meeting 22
  Central Committee on
    Community Medicine 140,
    142
  Committee on Encroachment
    23, 25

*General Medical Service for the
    Nation* 34
  Medical Planning Committee
    45
  opposition to state medicine
    17, 45
  Public Health Committee 119
  reaction to Seebohm Report
    107
  salary negotiator for MOsH
    17, 24
Buzzard, Sir Farquhar 37, 42

Cancer Act 1939 15
cancer clinics 16
Central Committee on
    Community Medicine 130
Chadwick, E. 1, 7, 10
child health 130
  responsibility of GPs 76
Children's Minimum Council 17,
    30, 31
chronically sick and disabled 2,
    82
clinical medicine
  relation with community
    medicine 22, 113
clinical MOs 59, 76, 119
clinicians 135–7
  opposition to MOsH 136
  status of 130
  training 44
clinics 1, 21, 23–4

GP control of 17, 23, 76
'Cogwheel' Report 113, 136
Collings Report 71
community care
    responsibility for 58
    and social work 59
community health councils 146
community medicine 2, 3, 4, 10
    administration 142–3
    conflicts in 106, 135, 162
    constraints on 3
    disillusionment with 125
    political implications 161
    problems of 134
    recruitment to 163
    resource allocation 143
    as specialty 11, 44, 101, 136,
        160
    transition to 11, 127, 163
    vs. clinical medicine 130
community physicians 2, 11, 28,
        75, 80, 100, 102
    accountability 146, 162
    advisory role 116, 140
    and district general hospitals
        112–13
    hierarchical relationship of
        112, 143, 144
    management role 140–3, 162
    monitoring role 126
    posts 125, 126
    and preventive medicine 146
    relationship to GPs 3
    role definition 102, 125, 135
        problems of 162
    specialists 125, 134, 135–6, 140
    status 125
    tasks 138
    three-tier structure 125
    trainees 144'
    watchdog role 30, 146
consensus management 11, 118,
        119

Consultative Council on Medical
    and Allied Services 18
corporate planning 127
coterminosity 111
Cox, Dr A. 22–3
Cranbrook Report 76
curative medicine 2, 22
    integration with preventive
        medicine 11, 18, 20, 43, 76,
        103, 147

Dawson Report 18, 19, 23
    reaction by public health
        doctors 20
District Community Physicians
    132, 133, 134
death rate *see* mortality
dentistry, preventive 31, 49
diploma in public health 80
district general hospitals 112
district medical committee 136
domicilary care 70, 71, 72
    of elderly 58
Duncan Report 142, 143

ecological approach to
    preventive medicine 119
education in health 5, 6, 16, 20,
        33, 71, 78, 147
    of mothers 20
Education Act 63
elderly, provision for 58, 82
encroachment 10, 17, 22, 24, 29,
        58, 75
environmental health 2, 5, 19, 32,
        62, 70, 78, 146
environmental hygiene 16, 45,
        78, 119
environmental sanitation 5, 6
epidemiology 11, 29, 40, 48, 78,
        80, 100, 101, 103, 114, 117,
        120, 143, 147
    research in 59

eugenics 29
Eugenics Society 89

Faculty of Community Medicine
    102, 119, 120, 126, 142, 161
family medicine 70–1, 76
Family Services Unit 90
family social work 106
food legislation 5

General Medical Council 21
general practice, state of 71
GPs 10
    access to under NHS 81
    independent status 10, 17,
        18–19, 22, 46
    integration with MOsH 72
    lack of facilities 71
    opposition to health clinics 74
    and preventive medicine 22
    role of 20
    service 45
    and social work 91
    standards 71
    vs. MOsH 10, 23, 58, 69, 72
germ theory 6, 8
Gillie Report 76, 91
Gilloran Report 115, 160
Grey Book 145
Griffiths Report 126–7, 149,
    151–2, 152–3
Grundy, F. 48, 59, 60, 78, 80
Guillebaud Report 63, 71

health centres 15, 16, 18, 46, 73
    concept of 74
health policy 4
health reform 3, 18
health services integration 116
health service personnel 165
health status 2, 100
health visitors 1, 16, 46, 66, 71–3,
    84, 89, 186

Health and Welfare Plan 58, 86
home help service 46, 60
home nursing 46
hospital administration 26–7, 28,
    47
hospital care 2, 3, 111, 135, 160
    costs 126
hospital management 10, 16, 63
Hospital Plan 58, 86
housing 5, 6, 32, 35, 161
Hunter Report 118, 119, 130
hygiene, domestic 6
hygiene, personal 5, 9, 19

immunization 16, 28, 29, 30, 46,
    147
industrialization 4
infant welfare 43, 45
infectious diseases 1, 45, 60
Ingleby Committee 85
Institute of Social Medicine 36
intervention strategies 105
isolation 5, 7, 28, 30

Jameson Report 89
juvenile delinquency 90

Kilbrandon Committee 85, 106

Lalonde Report 147
latched-on officers 129–30
legislation, enabling 4, 15
living standards 2
local authority responsibilities
    46
Local Government Act 1872 4
Local Government Act 1929 15,
    16, 24–6, 28
Local Government Act 1958 63,
    67
Local Government Commission
    67–8
local government reorganisation

1974 1
London School of Hygiene 42
Longford Report 85

Mallaby Report 83
malnutrition 17, 30, 31, 33
maternal and child welfare 2, 15,
    46, 62
Maternal and Child Welfare Act
    18
maternal and child welfare
    clinics 21
maternity services 71, 75, 76
maternal welfare 2, 15
Maud Report 83
medical administration 7, 29, 58,
    62, 78–80, 118, 161
Medical Inspection of School
    Children Act 1907 22
Medical Planning Research 36
medical politics 3, 8, 141
Medical Practitioners' Union 74
medical sociology 78, 80
mental health 45
mentally ill, provision for 2, 9,
    29, 58, 96, 107
    social work 108
midwifery, domicilary 16, 46
Ministry of Health 17, 19, 31, 33
Medical Officers of Health
    accountability 111
    administrative role 5, 19, 29,
        58, 75, 77, 141
    annual reports 5, 17, 30, 47, 60
    antipathy to *see* Dawson
        Report
    assistant 75
    county 46
    demotion of 130, 132
    district 63, 163
    divisional 67
    junior 66
    management role 110

mixed appointments 63
NHS reorganisation, effects of
    130–1
    powers of 4–5
    promotion 67
    public health doctors 3, 8, 9,
        19, 22–3; pay structure of 62
    role 21, 81, 141
    salary scale 48, 61
    senior 75
    and social work 89
    specialization 58, 79
    status 17, 24, 48, 60, 64, 135–6,
        143
    statutory responsibilities 19,
        58
    threat to GPs 10
    training 30, 80, 128, 141
morbidity 31, 101
    maternal 17, 33
Morris, J.N. 84, 101, 103–5, 140
mortality rate 6, 29, 31, 101
    infant 20, 30, 31, 32
municipal hospitals 1, 5, 10, 16,
    29

National Advisory Commission
    33
National Assistance Act 1948 83
national health insurance 20
national health service 1, 36, 44,
    70
    cost of 15, 71, 100
    financial crisis 125, 137, 162
    Green Paper 100
    integrated 45, 100, 126
    management policy 162
    morale in 162
    reorganisation 81, 100, 106,
        126, 132–41, 162
    effects on MOsH 130–1
    three-tier structure 2
    unification 131

White Paper 45, 46
National Health Service Act 4, 10, 16
national insurance 7, 34
National Unemployed Workers' Movement 31
Newman, Sir G. 19, 20, 22, 33, 71
Normanfield Hospital Inquiry 138-9
nutrition 30, 38, 49

obstetrics 76
Oxford Institute 40-1, 42, 43

panel system 20
parental responsibility 10, 71
Patients First 149-50
pay scale of MOsH 63
Peckham Health Centre 9, 17, 32, 35, 70
personal health services, responsibility for 62
poor law hospitals 9, 15, 24
poor law medicine, integrated administration 19
poor law MOs 10
population medicine 160
Porritt Report 79, 109
positive health 32, 34
post-natal care 31
preventive medicine 1, 8, 18, 20, 21, 119, 146-7
  GPs claim to 22-3
  vs. curative medicine 10
  progress of 28
preventive services 3
private practice 10, 17
  conflict with state medicine 58
problem families 89, 90
professional autonomy 10
programme budgeting 127
Proper Officer duties 139
public health 6, 7

activities 3
appropriate intervention 6
morale 111
philosophy 16-17
popular image 1
Public Health Acts 4, 6
  enforcement of 4-5
Public Health Congress 27
public health departments 91
  effects of NHS 44-5
  growth of 15
  loss of power 16
  statutory power 3, 5
public health inspectors 66

recruitment to public health 68
reform of local government 67, 68
regional hospital boards 74
Regional Medical Officers 125, 128-9, 134
residential care of elderly 58
Royal Commission on Dentists and Doctors' Pay 61
Royal Commission on Local Government 83, 111
Royal Commission on Medical Education 135
Ryle, J. 35, 37, 38, 40, 41, 43, 44

salary scales of MOsH 25
Sanitary Commission 1869 4
sanitary reform 5
sanitary science 78
sanitation 1, 5, 19
school health 15, 19, 45
school meals 31
school MOs 75
Specialists in Community Medicine 129, 130, 133, 134, 143
screening, mass 43, 147
Seebohm Committee 16, 65, 82,

84, 101, 107
    reaction to 106–9
Sheldon Report 76
sickness benefit 7
slum clearance 5
social medicine 35–44
    alienation from public health
        44
    concept of 17
    definition 37, 80
    MOsH responsibility for 82
social reform 6
social science 5, 26, 40
social services reform 84–5
social well-being 106
social work 82, 89
    separation from community
        medicine 16, 81
    principles 84
social workers 59, 66, 82–4,
        100
    and children 84
    and GPs 91
    lobby 59
Society of Medical Officers of
        Health 33, 43, 69
    evidence to Hunter
        Committee 115
    relation with BMA 24
    Seebohm Committee 107
staffing levels 83
state intervention 6, 7, 16
state medicine 16, 17, 18, 24, 28,
        36
    rejection of 161

state regulation 4

TB 1, 9, 15, 16, 28–9, 45, 47, 49
Titmuss, R.M. 35, 36, 39, 59, 71,
        80, 82, 84–6, 91, 100, 101,
        103, 106, 114
Todd Commission 44, 104, 110
treatment vs. prevention 22, 23

unemployment benefit 7, 31
unemployment, effects of 17, 30,
        49
unit management teams 150–1
urban degeneration 5, 7

vaccination 4, 16, 46
VD 1, 15, 45
voluntary hospitals 10, 17, 34, 46
voluntary organizations 10, 21,
        22

wartime conditions 36–7
Webb S. and B. 9–10
welfare reform 7, 82
welfare service 47
Whitley Council 48, 60
William Budd Health Centre 74
Women's Group on Public
        Welfare 31, 35, 90
Women's Health Inquiry 17, 31,
        33
women in medical practice 75

Younghusband Report 87, 89,
        109